SPEAKING OF THE ENVIRONMENT

SPEAKING OF THE ENVIRONMENT

WHAT YOUR SCIENCE CLASSES DIDN'T TEACH YOU ABOUT EFFECTIVE COMMUNICATION

PAULA JASINSKI
DAVE JASINSKI

NEW DEGREE PRESS

SPEAKING OF THE ENVIRONMENT

What Your Science Classes Didn't Teach You About Effective Communication

ISBN 978-1-63730-994-0 *Paperback*

978-1-63730-748-9 *Kindle Ebook*

978-1-63730-749-6 *Ebook*

TABLE OF CONTENTS

WELCOME

If you are a scientist, environmental advocate, student, or other practitioner who works on environmental management, restoration, protection, conservation, and education—we are glad you are here. We wrote this book for you. We understand you. We have either been in your position or worked closely with others who have. We are trained scientists who have had the good fortune to see and harness the power of effective communication, and we want to share our experience and communication approaches so that you can use them in your own work.

There is an urgent need to get things right concerning environmental affairs, for our own sake and that of the natural world. Environmental protections safeguard what we need and love. In turn, creating and maintaining those protections depends upon the ability of environmental advocates and scientists to make the case for a healthy environment in ways that resonate with the public and decision makers.

> Science classes develop scientists but not, in large part, effective communicators.

However, the value and art of communication is not part of most scientific training, even though it is essential to close the gap on environmental action. Science classes develop scientists but not, in large part, effective communicators. This gap leads to scientists who understand the issues and the range of solutions but not necessarily how to inform public opinion or change behaviors. Everyone suffers the consequences of this, from responding (or not) to climate change, a pandemic, or even preserving green space in your local community. While communication skills are only part of the equation, how scientists and environmental advocates talk about data and research makes a big difference in public perceptions and other outcomes.

We wrote this book because, with over five decades of experience between us, we have been in the trenches of marketing and communicating about science and environmental issues. We want to share what we have learned to help you reach your goals. One book might not help you win every battle; however, we certainly hope you can use this one to understand how you can communicate differently and to develop new techniques for how you engage with others.

HOW WE COMMUNICATE MATTERS

How environmental advocates and scientists speak about the environment *matters*. The way we frame our goals, the messages we relay, the words we use, the images we share—all of these have the power to help us reach environmental goals or push people away.

Currently, along with COVID-19 and climate change, scientists tell us we're at a tipping point in terms of environmental degradation, land conversion, species extinction, and greenhouse gas emissions. We don't have much more time to get things "right." As climate changes cascade across our planet to fundamentally disrupt life as we know it, we must get smarter and savvier about getting people to make changes.

As the scientists who developed the 2021 Intergovernmental Panel on Climate Change report indicate, our collective hope now lies in urgent and widespread policy and lifestyle changes (IPCC, 2021). How likely are those changes unless we can connect with even more people?

ENVIRONMENTAL END POINTS ARE OFTEN NOT THE SELLING POINTS

Scientists and environmental advocates aren't typically selling goods and services in the traditional sense, but they are selling ideas and hoping to influence hearts and minds. The more we can learn how to listen, learn, and incorporate, the easier it will become to engage others to care as much as we do.

We know this because this is what we do every day at Green Fin Studio. Effective environmental communication is not always about convincing people to care about an issue for reasons that are important to *you*. It's about convincing them to care about an issue for reasons that are important to *them*.

The importance of this is illustrated in a project that we developed for the US Environmental Protection Agency's (EPA) Chesapeake Bay Program Office.

Within the mid-Atlantic region, the Chesapeake Bay Program has a goal to restore eighty-three thousand acres of wetlands on farmland across its watershed. When we began this project, very little progress on that goal had been made. Many state and federal agencies provide funding for farmers to create wetlands on their land. The goal is to increase habitat, biodiversity, and improve water quality in streams and rivers. However, none of this can be realized if farmers can't find the funding programs in the first place or understand why they should even consider creating a wetland. Our task was to help develop a website that would serve as an information hub for agricultural landowners interested in restoring wetlands on their property.

In addition to approaching the project as scientists, cataloging evidence of how wetland restoration works, and how wetlands benefit landowners and the local environment, we also listened to the farmers. In fact, we personally talked to about one hundred farmers and others who regularly work with the regional farming community.

One farmer we spoke with put it succinctly: "Don't sell me on the value of wetlands, sell me on why they're valuable to me."

In other words, we should not expect farmers to convert working acreage into wetlands for broad regional water quality goals without considering what's in it for them. With this in mind, we found that farmers were very interested in hearing about wetland benefits such as improving water management on their farms, attracting pollinators, and providing new recreational opportunities. Wetland restoration programs provided all of those and more. We made sure that these benefits were featured prominently on the website. We also focused on the monetary value of wetlands in terms of the services they provide. The environmental benefits that the Bay Program is interested in were also featured but put on equal footing with economic benefits.

We should note that the farmers we spoke to did care about water quality and the impact of farms on local waters. Almost all of them were already employing other practices to reduce their impact to water quality. When you ask a farmer to take land out of production, you are asking them to keep money out of their pocket, so your reasons should be both compelling and practical.

One Friday afternoon shortly after the Wetlands Work website launched, Paula received a call from a gentleman who had a sense of urgency in his voice: "Hello, I'm with the US Department of Agriculture (USDA) and I'm looking for whomever created the wetlands restoration tool created for farmers."

She responded that we, Green Fin Studio, had developed the tool with the EPA and the Chesapeake Bay Program partners. She was bracing for a critique over something we might have missed.

"Well, I just wanted to say that one of the farmers I work with told me about it earlier this week. He was able to quickly find technical assistance and funding programs that met his needs. Since then, I've spent a few days looking at it, and it is terrific. The fact that a farmer told me about it speaks volumes."

The person on the phone had worked at USDA for fifteen years and had been frustrated at how difficult it was for farmers to navigate the myriad of programs that fund wetland restoration projects.

So why had so many of us missed these connections in the past? We think it was because environmental advocates were taking the approach of "I need to convince you to create wetlands for the same reasons that I care about wetlands" instead of "Here are some practical benefits that wetlands offer you as a landowner."

What we found in this project has direct applicability to many other programs. The reasons and motivations behind achieving environmental goals need to directly connect with your target audience. You must consider why those who need to act should care and what's in it for them.

We have found that, as environmentalists, we can be a lot more successful by identifying these selling points to meet our end goals. They might include quality of life, community character, safe drinking water, recreational opportunities, job training, attracting new businesses and residents, educational programming, human health, or access to renewable energy. Environmental programs often offer these co-benefits even though environmentalists have not traditionally made them the strong selling points they could be.

MAKING CONNECTIONS FOR CHANGE

The marketing world has long known that understanding audiences is critical. Scientists and environmentalists have largely been missing that part. Without understanding who you are talking to, it's nearly impossible to connect with them about why they should care, even when they are directly impacted and stand to benefit from helping to affect change.

We have found that when you get to know your audiences, you can establish connections that lead to real change. Our planet is at an environmental tipping point. Science offers hope for the future, and environmental communication can translate that science to the change we need.

As scientists and communicators, we need to inform the collective understanding in order to change behaviors on how our human fate is directly tied to environmental health. This is especially important while the political pendulum swings wildly between taking aggressive approaches to implement environmental protections and taking aggressive approaches to dismantle environmental protections. That said, we acknowledge legislation alone is not the answer.

Environmental regulations protect us and our natural systems, but even with those in place we're not going to reach our goals until we can find a better way to communicate with each other. Environmental communication must bridge political divides, religious differences, socioeconomic diversity, and more if we are to have hope for the future.

WHAT YOU WILL FIND HERE

In 2010, when we launched our environmental communication firm, Green Fin Studio, we had a vision to connect marketing and communication practices in support of environmental priorities. We did not know anyone else working at that intersection at the time. Luckily, the field is growing as more people discover this fascinating intersection. Over the years, we've learned a lot through trial and error, from other practitioners, artists, and from leaders and doers in just about every other field imaginable.

We are sharing much of what we have learned along the way. In the coming chapters, we discuss:

- How understanding your audience can become your superpower
- Why and how to avoid jargon
- How to structure powerful narratives
- The power of visual communications
- How to put the pieces into action

Throughout this book, we've included case studies and resources to inspire you to apply these ideas to your own projects. Each chapter also has a few take-home tips to summarize its lessons and serve as a quick reference guide.

This is the book we wished we'd had years ago. Our hope is that this book helps others start much further ahead than we did or just provides you with new ways of thinking about existing problems.

CHAPTER ONE

THE ART AND URGENCY OF ENVIRONMENTAL COMMUNICATION

"The only possible way to get somebody to change is to reach into their hearts."

—JANE GOODALL

Our planet is at a crossroads. Unless scientists can close the communication gap to broader audiences, it seems unreasonable to expect major progress on the big issues. Climate change, environmental injustices, toxic chemicals in our drinking water, deforestation, destruction of wetlands, collapsing fisheries, unprecedented rates of species extinctions, energy crises, and declining air quality are just some of the ongoing environmental emergencies that motivate us to find better ways to communicate with people on the other side of the gap.

If you are reading this book, you are probably already keenly aware of the urgency to have more people embrace and act on scientific information and guidance. We are not the first to note that regardless of your level of comfort with interacting with broader audiences, the time for more effective science and environmental communication is now. Realistically, decades ago would have been better, but since we cannot rewrite history, this is where we are.

Amid the challenges ahead and the potential for crises fatigue, we are reminded of a Cameron Crowe quote about the character, Lloyd, from his *Say Anything* movie: "Optimism is a revolutionary act." Indeed. You need more than a healthy dose of optimism to devote your time, love, and passion toward environmental and humanitarian causes. Environmental communication is our chosen form of optimism, and it often feels revolutionary.

We think of environmental communication as science communication through a social lens—where science often meets society, including food production, water access and quality, renewable energy development, land planning and conservation, climate change impacts, and so much more. Environmental communication must bridge political divides and religious differences and become more inclusive to represent a wider diversity of communities and consider the social science of motivating actions if we are to have hope for the future. Our focus is primarily on those of you working directly on environmental issues, but our methods can be adapted for communicators in other scientific disciplines to use.

Why haven't previous public engagement efforts around environmental issues been more effective at shaping decisions to help us avoid these crises? One reason is that scientific input is only one factor in decision making. Economics, regulatory authorities, human behavior, political influence, selfish or short-sighted motives, and more come into play as well. However, environmental advocates and scientists must also bear a portion of the responsibility as, historically, their methods of outreach and communication have not always been terribly effective at influencing decisions.

Facts are valuable currency within the scientific community. Scientific facts are established through repeated observations and experimentation. Scientists try to reproduce each other's findings to be sure those facts are indeed actual facts. Then scientists share those facts with others outside of the scientific community to increase awareness. This step is where we can miss opportunities for meaningful communication.

Because informational transactions in the scientific community are brokered in facts, there is a common misconception among scientists that just by presenting the facts to the public and decision-makers they will understand an issue and behaviors will change. This way of thinking is sometimes referred to as the information deficit model, that a deficit of information is the primary barrier to behavior change. The basic assumption is that a primary approach to problems, including those as complex as climate change, is to present people with facts and data. Spoiler alert: This rarely works.

People are not always motivated by facts and data about an issue. They are more motivated by how the issue impacts them. Sometimes, just closing the gap in knowledge does work, especially when your goal is to increase awareness. However, if your goal goes beyond raising awareness to motivate action, simply providing information probably won't work.

Think about it. If we just needed facts to guide our choices, we'd all be eating perfectly balanced diets and religiously wearing sunscreen, and no one would smoke. Most of us know what the data tells us about these choices, but people aren't entirely rational when it comes to decisions, even about their own health. Emotions, what our peers think, personal circumstances, and other factors come into play.

So how do we reach more people, establish trust, and influence decisions? We must have a better understanding of our own goals, our audiences and what they value, and how our goals can align with these values. Once you have made those connections, a multitude of options for engaging with your audiences will be available. Storytelling is one option, detailed in chapter five, that we embrace for its ability to emotionally connect and resonate with people. Data visualization, see chapter six, is another powerful method.

We have seen this play out in the evolution of geographic information systems (GIS). Data portals around environmental topics used to be all the rage. Anyone could create their own maps with a few clicks of a mouse. What could be more powerful than giving people access to facts by way of layer upon layer of spatial data? (Sounds like the information deficit model.) The answer to that question was stories. Data portals can be overwhelming for users lacking technical background in the data layers, the specific map viewer application, or even knowing what questions they can answer with all that information.

So ESRI, one of the leading GIS software companies, developed StoryMaps to combine the emotional capability of storytelling with the facts of spatial data. StoryMaps allow space for interpretive content, photos, and videos that can appeal to audience priorities and values. Instead giving people a bunch of maps and saying, "You figure it out," StoryMaps are built to guide users through a narrative and draw their attention to maps that enforce points made in the story.

BRAND AID

If you work within a scientific discipline, you likely understand the broad range of scientific career options. The public, however, largely identifies "science" as a brand without nuanced distinctions between the myriad scientific disciplines. As with all brands, it carries a certain identity.

What do you think of when you hear the words Apple, Google, Amazon, Facebook, or Starbucks? These brands have become household names, and we associate certain imagery, words, and feelings with them. Those feelings, positive or negative, define a brand. Corporate marketing promotes what an organization wants people to feel about a brand. The collective public perception shaped by user experiences is what really shapes a brand.

What do you think of when you think of science? What images do you conjure? What images do you think others conjure? Do you see beakers and test tubes? A chalkboard of formulas? Someone collecting water samples? A computer modeler?

According to the organization ScienceCounts, science's brand is hope. In their 2018 Benchmark study, they polled 2,021 Americans and asked what word they most closely associated with the word "science." Sixty-three percent answered "hope." That was far more than any other word associated with science, including "fear," "joy," or "boredom."

What could be more important these days than hope?

Hope is a powerful emotion. Maybe people hope for clean water for their families, lower energy bills, and access to affordable and healthy food. Knowing that your brand, the thing you have devoted your life to, represents hope to others is extremely powerful.

Despite the fire hose of negative news around the state of our environment, people think science can help solve some of the big issues in front of us. Society sees science as the answer, but how does science interact with society?

The same ScienceCounts study found that while the public sees science's brand as hope, slightly more scientists themselves see it as "joy." Most of us got into the field of science and environmental work because it was something we took great personal pride in, and we enjoyed it. While 40 percent of scientists surveyed associated "joy" with science, only 6 percent of the public did. We think one reason for this may be that all too few scientists and environmentalists remember to share the sheer joy we find in our work with others, for fear of coming off as "unprofessional" or "not serious," or perhaps because the magnitude of environmental crises can be overwhelming. Joy in our work and successes is abundant, and hope and joy are attractive qualities in winning over other hearts and minds to accomplish even more.

MEET ME AT THE LOADING DOCK

In a conversation with Laura Lindenfeld, executive director of the Alan Alda Center for Communicating Science, we talked about how to bridge the divide between research and social applications of that research. She brought up the concept of how many scientists see themselves as delivering science to a metaphorical loading dock, where they hope someone will come and pick it up and apply it (Cash, 2006).

Many applied researchers, communication specialists, and others actively work to transfer science. New initiatives for delivering "broader impacts" have also been developed to push researchers into the role of making science relevant to social issues or to work with others to make those connections.

As Lindenfeld noted, "You've got those who produce research, you've got the applied researchers who are going to help bring it to the people. The hope is the people are going to get it and their behaviors can change, but it just doesn't work that way."

The researchers developing the stuff for the loading dock usually haven't started by asking anyone in society what they care about or need, or how they would use the resulting information. Sometimes, it's the funding sources that ask for specific products without first engaging the potential users about their utility or application.

We should all want to close this gap. The more relevant science can be to societal issues, the more support scientists will have. More support means more funding for needed research. Environmental communication helps make connections between the findings of research and the wants and needs of society.

At least one person reading this book is going to stop here and think, "Wait a minute. I got into science for the joy of discovery, and many scientific contributions were found through blue-sky thinking." Absolutely. Einstein is an example of a scientist who wasn't necessarily driven by specific applied research but instead by understanding how the world works. There will always be room for this type of science. In other words, keep on being you, because sometimes a scientific discovery develops something the rest of the world couldn't have imagined before, much less developed an applied research program for. In the end, though, hopefully we end up in the same place: with something we want to share with the world. Maybe it will make lives and the planet healthier, more efficient, and more sustainable.

MOVING BEYOND WISHFUL THINKING

Antoine de Saint-Exupéry wrote, "A goal without a plan is just a wish." We all have plans for most things in life: vacation schedules, retirement, proposal development, and even grocery shopping. Because if we don't, we might be very unhappy with the results.

With a little planning and communication insight, reaching environmental and programmatic goals can be a lot easier. As we mentioned above, communicating strategically is about more than just trying to increase awareness about an issue. Simply just teaching people about science or the environment does not mean people will change their attitudes or behaviors. If you really want to change behaviors, from individual to collective actions, you need to be strategic about the way you develop and implement outreach.

Plans provide detailed road maps, a series of milestones or objectives, to achieve a desired result. The same is true for environmental communications. No major brand would begin marketing a product without a plan and clear goals. Marketing and communications are how companies connect directly with potential customers and encourage them to make a purchasing decision. Communication is what customers are told about a product or program. Marketing refers to how that information is shared or advertised so that it answers the question of why someone should care.

The science communication research team of John Besley (Ellis N. Brandt Professor, Michigan State University) and Anthony Dudo (Associate Professor, Moody College of Communication, University of Texas at Austin) provides guidance for scientists on developing strategic communication. If you have not yet seen their June 2019 webinar "Strategic Science Communication: A Social Scientific Approach to Public Engagement," hosted by the Alan Alda Center for Communicating Science, you should take time to watch it online.

Besley and Dudo were both professional communicators who went on to obtain their PhDs and are now on a mission to help scientists communicate more effectively. They surveyed scientists and found that some of the most important engagement goals are to ensure that policy makers use scientific evidence, have society value science, encourage others to pursue scientific careers, and build support for research funding. It would be hard to accomplish any of those goals without a strategic communication plan that includes tactics (how you'll accomplish your goals) and investments in building trusted relationships with your audiences.

Besley and Dudo compared the cultivation of public engagement in science to the Slow Food movement. If you are not familiar, the Slow Food movement developed in response to the popularity of fast food which is not healthy for people or the environment. In turn, the researchers urge other scientists to think about science communication as a process, bearing more effective results from thoughtful planning over time rather than thinking of it like a "hot dog stand" that delivers quick bites that are not very enriching. Taking a long-term approach not only allows you to be more strategic in your planning and delivery, it also has the added benefit of helping to build trusted relationships with your audiences.

The best possible solution is to consider communication as a first step, not a final one. Plan for how your results will be communicated and disseminated at the outset. By outset we mean the proposal phase. This will ensure that funds exist to make this communication happen. Many in research fields hope their findings will make it out to wider audiences and be used for societal good. Hope is a terrific thing to have, but hope is not a strategy.

YES, AND...

Here's an example of how important it is to communicate about environmental science, for the environment's sake, for society's sake, and for program survival. In 2012, during our first meeting with a team of senior ocean researchers from the National Oceanic and Atmospheric Administration (NOAA), they expressed frustration that almost every year Congress threatened to reduce their funding levels. "They don't even know what we do," one of them lamented.

"People know the National Weather Service, but they don't understand all that we're doing to protect oceans or fisheries."

"That's why we called you," one of the team members explained. "We would like you to develop a series of white papers around our science programs. We're thinking maybe a series of fifteen to twenty white papers, and then we can take them to Congress to help them understand what we do."

"White papers?" we asked, keeping in mind that these researchers are world renowned for the truly cutting-edge science they conduct and how it has been used to protect coastal regions and maintain healthy ecosystems. White papers are somewhere between a scientific journal article and a news article meant for public consumption. While they aim to explain complex topics for lay audiences, they typically lack narrative and emotional connections.

That's when we put on our improv hats. "Yes, and... we have some other ideas," we responded.

We knew that Apple had recently launched their iBooks Author software, allowing us to create an e-book that could be distributed through the Apple store. We also knew that many states had established mandates for teachers to rely more on tablet-based curricula and to provide locally relevant environmental education materials.

We saw the stars aligning to bring all these things together in a way that addressed NOAA's needs. They had been thinking of members of key congressional committee staff as an important audience they needed to impress. They were right, as Congress holds the purse strings. Yet to really influence elected officials, we wanted to help them create products their constituents would want.

We knew that teachers around the Chesapeake Bay were hungry for credible and easily accessible environmental education materials. We also knew there was a wealth of NOAA science and data waiting to be interpreted through interactive graphics, maps, and data explorers. These elements could be combined into a users' guide, of sorts, to the Chesapeake Bay. The complexities of the Chesapeake Bay ecosystem would be explained using imagery and easy-to-understand text. A broad audience would understand how the Bay works and NOAA's role in the research.

Luckily, the team from NOAA embraced the idea. We spent the next year developing the "Chesapeake Bay Ecosystem Atlas," a visual guide to how the Bay works—using NOAA's science. We hired a small group of stellar science teachers to guide our work so that it could seamlessly flow into classrooms around the Bay region.

Instead of just developing their white papers, we also developed a very interactive, digital textbook. Guess which product is being used in middle and high schools across six states and the District of Columbia and that school administrators now associate with NOAA and that elected officials were happiest with? Okay, all of these questions are rhetorical, but you get the point. Data visualization and storytelling were home runs with their target audiences.

The Chesapeake Bay Ecosystem Atlas is available for free download from the iTunes link listed in our Resources section below. Effective communication products add value to scientists' work and support their overall organizational goals. All too often environmental communication is an afterthought or a one-off, without considering how it fits into their larger vision. Developing the digital Atlas took more time than a series of white papers; however, the result was far more valuable to a public audience and NOAA, in terms of promoting its brand.

COMMUNICATING STRATEGICALLY

We encourage you to consider how environmental communication can support your organizational plan and individual project goals. Developing a strategic communication plan provides a framework for that. What are the key elements of a strategic environmental communication plan? Here is what we call the Five Ws that we believe are foundational to the formation of a strong communication plan.

1. **WHY** should someone else care about what you're doing? This little three letter word poses a huge question and can provide powerful insights. Asking why someone else should care about your work helps you define your value proposition to others. Simon Sinek, author of *Start with Why*, gave a TED talk in 2009 that has inspired more than fifty-six million people to ask themselves to define their own "why" and address their motives or purpose. If you haven't read his book or seen his TED talk, we highly recommend both for their ability to inspire your communication plan.
2. **WHAT** do you want as outcomes of broader engagement? You might have several objectives for your communication,

from increasing awareness about a topic, spurring conversation with and between audiences, framing an issue, changing behaviors, incorporating science into decision making, attracting new students or staff, highlighting your own role in the field, securing funding, and more. What needs to happen for you to reach your goal?

3. **WHO** needs to understand the relevance of your information and act for you to be successful? Do you need to engage homeowners, students, farmers, fishermen, elected officials, funders, or others? Identifying the human element helps you understand which relationships are vital to your success. Additionally, knowing who your target audiences are will help you align specific messages for each one of them.
4. **WHEN** do you need something to happen? You may want to accomplish several outcomes, and each one may have an associated timeframe from short-term to long-term. This step helps you prioritize and plan for your communication pieces.
5. **WHERE** will your messages be shared? Does your work have geographic specificity that delineates where you should focus? Will a digital campaign through social media or direct email reach your target audiences? Or would a meeting or conference be the best place to connect with those you want to reach?

Remember, environmental communication is a tool to help you meet your goals, not a goal in and of itself. The following chapters provide what we see as fundamentals in effective communication, but only you can answer how that supports your larger strategy.

CHAPTER ONE TAKE HOME TIPS

1. In the face of big challenges, remember that having "optimism is a revolutionary act."
2. Facts alone rarely change hearts and minds.
3. Connect with your audiences on an emotional level by speaking to what they care about in order to understand what might motivate them to change.
4. Consider communication as a first step, not a final one.
5. Use your communication efforts to support your overall programmatic goals.
6. Address the Five Ws listed above to guide your strategic communication plan.
7. Look for specific audiences to connect with to help you amplify your message, like the example we provided of working with high school science teachers.

RESOURCES

1. Visit the Alan Alda Center for Communicating Science website at: AldaCenter.org for resources and training opportunities.
2. Learn more about ArcGIS StoryMaps and be inspired to create at: StoryMaps.arcgis.com
3. Download our free Chesapeake Bay Ecosystem Atlas to see how we used NOAA science to create an in-classroom text at: *bit.ly/ChesBayAtlasTeacher*
4. Join over fifty-six million other viewers and watch Simon Sinek's TEDxPugetSound talk, "How great leaders inspire action" at: *www.TED.com/Talks/Simon_Sinek_How_Great_Leaders_Inspire_Action*
5. Watch "Strategic Science Communication: A Social Scientific Approach to Public Engagement" webinar by

Anthony Dudo and John C. Besley at: *www.YouTube.com/watch?v=C5fqUJcswJQ*

CHAPTER TWO

LISTEN TO LEARN

"When you talk, you are only repeating what you already know. But if you listen, you may learn something new."

—THE DALAI LAMA XIV

Almost every environmental communication effort we have been involved with includes a discussion about how to reach beyond the proverbial choir; how to connect with those not already engaged. It may sound counterintuitive, but if you want new and different people to hear your messages, you must first listen to those who you want to listen to you.

When we take the time to listen to someone else, we almost always learn something. We might learn what the world looks like from where they sit, what they value, or what barriers exist, or maybe that they know an awful lot about an issue, including possible solutions we had yet to consider. By listening with empathy, you can gain a better understanding of how others view you and your priorities. Individual realities shape the lens through which we see others, fairly or unfairly. If you can incorporate listening to stakeholders into your process, that will help you find ways to build bridges, collaborate, and work toward broadly supported solutions.

For example, if you know your audience places a priority on economic over ecological concerns, invest the time to understand and address costs and benefits. Are there opportunities that provide both economic and ecological advantages? If you cannot address what your audience sees as either requirements or hurdles, it's going to be difficult to convince them to move in your direction.

Think of it this way: You already know that language can be a barrier in communication. If two people don't speak the same language, it's going to be hard for them to communicate. Environmental communication is the same idea. If someone else doesn't prioritize environmental health in their decision making, it's going to be difficult for you to communicate unless you look for what you may have in common. The key is to look for mutually beneficial outcomes, whether they are in the short-term or long-term. Taking the time to dig into what they believe and value almost always sheds light on possible ways forward that will help you be more successful.

Cultivating this type of empathy can facilitate productive working relationships and the ability to reach consensus decisions faster. As illustrated in the figure below, having empathy supports conversations, knowledge sharing, trust, and, ultimately, a pathway to developing solutions.

Empathy Builds a Path to Solutions

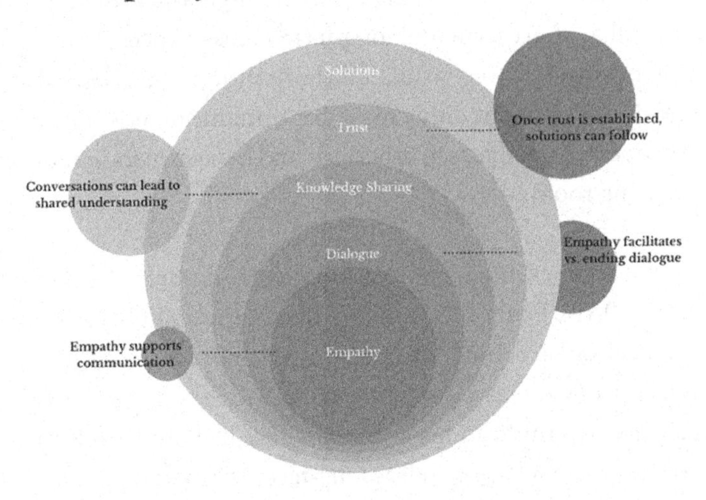

HI, I'M WITH THE GOVERNMENT, AND I'M HERE TO LISTEN

When Paula began working with the National Oceanic and Atmospheric Administration (NOAA) as a fisheries biologist, part of her job included representing the agency at regulatory hearings. The discussions ranged from setting fish harvest limits, restoration methods, and coastal development permits. All these decisions impacted people's lives in a very real way, from what they could or couldn't do on their properties to how or if they could make a living.

Her scientific education and training had taught her to read and understand jargon-filled literature, analyze data, and generally "speak science." Though nothing in her professional development, to date, had prepared her to listen with empathy to the other speakers, including those not trained as scientists.

There was, and is, a need to talk about collective versus individual costs, benefits, and impacts of regulatory decisions, as well as short-term and long-term consequences. Having the perspective to consider all those things and science in rendering opinions didn't make her immune to the very real, very personal impacts to fishermen and homeowners in those hearing rooms.

One winter evening, not long after she had started working for NOAA, Paula was tasked with presenting the science and rationale behind keeping an area of oyster reefs closed to harvest. It was a contentious decision with immediate economic ramifications to those whose livelihoods depend on oyster harvests, as well as long-term implications for population recovery, habitat restoration, and the investment of public funds. Opening the area for harvest had the potential to undo a couple of years' worth of federally funded restoration work. Following the hearing that resulted in keeping the area closed, Paula had to be escorted to her vehicle by armed guards because the oyster harvesters certainly didn't appreciate her data or recommendations. To them, she was "the government," there to tell them what they could and couldn't do, and they rejected her. Making decisions based on public, long-term benefits is rarely appreciated by those immediately and negatively impacted.

After that experience, she started arriving at meetings a lot earlier to spend time talking with harvesters and others before the hearings. Sometimes those conversations were about policy or monitoring data. Sometimes they were about children, pets, weather, how business was going, and other things that allowed everyone to just get to know each other on a personal level. Regardless of the topic, they were all meaningful.

She wondered if anyone on her side of the table had ever taken the time to really listen to those who were directly impacted by regulations and permitting decisions. When she spent time with them, they were able to talk about how some small changes in policies could help them and still protect resources.

All too often, science is not delivered as part of a conversation around needs and solutions, and then we, as scientists, are frustrated when people are not listening.

Among the interesting things she learned was that many commercial fishers wanted the option to report their harvest electronically. An online reporting option would greatly reduce their time filling out paperwork and give them easy access to historical catch data. Electronic reporting also helps environmental managers understand conditions at near real-time so they can respond quickly. However, no one had discussed the topic, making an assumption that fishers wouldn't embrace technology. This work was made possible because commercial fishers, Virginia Sea Grant, Environmental Defense Fund, and Virginia Marine Resources Commission also believed in and supported the process. Having empathy in this situation led to the creative solution of having fishers work with the state's electronic reporting team to add in features and functionality that improved their user experience. After those changes were made, the fishers involved led trainings to show other fishermen and fisherwomen that online reporting was both easy and beneficial. That led to a

270 percent increase in the number of fishermen using the online system in one year.

Whenever we listen to audiences, from local government leaders to farmers to fishers, not only have we come away with a much better understanding of their values and priorities, we have found they are also far more willing to engage in meaningful conversation and work collaboratively on solutions.

In the past, scientific training has not typically included any form of formal communication training apart from preparing scientific journal articles and giving presentations to other scientists. This is changing for the better. As we'll discuss throughout the book, scientists are increasingly now learning about the importance of engaging through improv, humor, and various media. We can't afford to ignore the importance of effective communication across broad audiences if we are to successfully tackle the challenges ahead.

"YOU'RE AN IDIOT" IS NOT AN EFFECTIVE CONVERSATION STARTER

Dr. Katharine Hayhoe, an effective climate change communicator, has seen more than her fair share of hecklers and climate deniers. Some of her audiences essentially try to shut down the conversation by telling her that she and the world's scientists are wrong. In a 2016 interview with the *New York Times*, Dr. Hayhoe says, "If you begin a conversation with, 'You're an idiot,' that's the end of the conversation too." Instead, Dr. Hayhoe encourages dialogue with empathy while still clearly providing the science behind climate change.

Approaches to environmental communication is not a one size fits all. Hayhoe uses data from trusted sources combined with her Christian faith to engage and calmly listen to audiences. Her approach provides the opportunity for others to speak up. When someone talks, they may share insight into their values, who they do and don't trust, what they are afraid of, and other information that's useful for seeking common ground.

In contrast, Dr. Michael Mann, a climate scientist at Penn State University, does not shy away from combatting lies and disinformation. In the same *New York Times* interview, he notes, "There is also a role for an approach that takes bad actors to task, naming names when it comes to the worst climate villains, those who are knowingly misleading the public and policy makers. Such an approach doesn't necessarily endear oneself to the hard-core climate change deniers, but it does help to expose the deceit, and in my view it is important for the public to know about that."

Mann and Hayhoe both offer valid approaches. Seek dialogue around facts and solutions whenever possible, but don't be afraid to call out misinformation, either.

ACTIVE LISTENING

In 2020, Green Fin Studio was hired to help the New England Fishery Management Council (NEFMC) communicate about a different way to manage fisheries. Most fisheries around the world are managed as single stocks, meaning there are specific guidelines for fishermen who fish for a particular species, say flounder, as a singular commodity. These guidelines may dictate when, where, how, and how much flounder can be caught in a given year without consideration for what other animals eat flounder, water quality, habitat conditions, or other ecosystem factors. Scientists around the world now advocate for changing that in such a way that larger ecosystem impacts and interactions are incorporated into management through ecosystem based fisheries management, or EBFM (Howell et al., 2021). Our team was brought on to help the NEFMC both explain the concept of EBFM and gauge reactions to the concept.

The first thing we did after reviewing available scientific material was begin talking to the people who would be impacted by a change to fisheries management. We interviewed close to one hundred people from multiple audience types across the Northeast region. We spoke with all types of fishermen, people involved in offshore wind, marine mammal experts, seafood markets, restaurants, local government officials, consumers, charter boat captains, and more. We listened to learn about what they already knew about or thought about EBFM and what a change would mean to them. Several interviewees were adamant that they or the environment would be worse off if the changes went forward while also admitting they weren't happy with the status quo, either. Those were the people we spent the most time talking to, because while it's exceptionally easy to criticize decisions, it's much harder to roll up your sleeves and help contribute to solutions. By taking the time to listen to them, everyone had a chance not just to provide an opinion but also either identify suggestions for solutions or accept they didn't have any better ideas.

The large suite of communication products that we developed are now being used in stakeholder engagement meetings across the region. These incorporate the themes that fishermen and other environmental advocates value, including how climate changes will impact the future of fishing and the environment and how stakeholder input can continually be incorporated into the process. See more on how we supported this project in chapter four, Just Say No to Jargon.

From fisheries management, climate change, biodiversity protections, habitat conservation, sustainable farming, to renewable energy, the big environmental issues of our time are challenging. The science behind each of them is complex, let alone trying to communicate that specific science and reach broad public consensus on solutions. Clearly, what got us to this point isn't what's going to lead us out. We need to look at our problems from new perspectives and look for solutions that range from groundbreaking new technologies to how we can just get better at communicating with one another.

Listening with empathy doesn't mean losing one's objectivity or losing sight of the bigger goals. It's one of the best ways we know to help you reach those goals. Effectively listening to others isn't a box to check so you can move on to something else. It requires building trusted relationships with your audiences so you can trust what they are telling you and then adaptively incorporate it into your approach. Engaging others to understand helps you empathize with what's important to them. When you know more about their values, barriers, and benefits, it will help develop a strategy that's more likely to resonate with them.

Do your audiences value having some flexibility in decisions that affect private property? That's good to know and may help you think about what land use options are compatible with wetland restoration, putting an easement in place, or taking some other action. Your communication efforts can then reflect what you learned, so your response is tailored to your audience's needs and concerns. Because outreach strategies should never be stagnant, it's always wise to incorporate an evaluation phase that helps you assess what worked and what didn't, and then adapt your approach for a next iteration.

CHAPTER TWO TAKE HOME TIPS

1. Listen to learn, not just to respond.
2. Listening with empathy is a superpower that helps you become a much better communicator.
3. Never assume you know what your audience thinks or wants before listening to them. Whenever possible, ask them directly. They are very likely to surprise you.
4. People make decisions based on their own self-interests, so be sure to convey how your work helps them, not just the environment.

CHAPTER THREE

CONNECTING YOUR AUDIENCE AND MESSAGES

"When you speak to everyone, you speak to no one."

—MEREDITH HILL

Most environmentalists and scientists we work with are fueled by passion. They got into their line of work not for fame and fortune, but because it is deeply meaningful to them. So, it follows they want to share that passion with the world, and they often do. Sometimes all 176 slides of that passion.

We support your passion, the joyful enthusiasm you have for your work. We just urge you to convey it in ways that are relevant, applicable, and even emotional to your audiences. The word "emotional" might make some of you uncomfortable because scientists are taught to be analytical and guard the scientific process, so it remains defensible. Conducting research, however, is much different than trying to communicate research and its relevance to non-scientific audiences.

Environmental communication is, at its core, a marriage between the cool, rational world of science and data and the more emotional world of marketing that seeks to engage audiences and change behaviors.

How you take science and use it to build engaging storylines to motivate people around specific actions and outcomes is the essence of environmental communication.

We are unabashed fans of TED (Technology, Entertainment, and Design) talks. There are several talks that we regularly rewatch and never fail to inspire; some of these are mentioned throughout this book. The TED structure of having a lone speaker on stage, with no podium to hide behind, to present deeply engaging stories in under twenty minutes has really set the standard for powerful presentations.

This is why we sought out TED's own Director of Speaker Coaching Briar Goldberg to learn her secrets. It's obvious she knows a thing or two about effective communication. She summarizes what she sees as an essential first step in her "golden rule" of communication. That rule is audience before content, or ABC, that she actually learned from one of her early mentors, Jim Wagstaffe.

In an interview with Ideas.Ted.com, Goldberg explains it this way: "Most of us actually communicate in the wrong direction. By wrong direction, I mean we draft our talking points, we build our PowerPoint slides, and fire off emails *before* we stop and ask ourselves, 'What does my audience expect out of this communication? Why are they taking time out of their busy days to listen to me?' Here's the deal: If your audience doesn't see themselves in your presentation, or doesn't care about your meeting, or, worse yet, if they don't understand how your pitch applies to them, then there's no point to opening your mouth! That's why the best communicators *always* think about their audiences before their content."

Wise advice. So, before you develop your next presentation, website, outreach campaign, or for that matter, any communication materials, consider your ABC. Think about who your audience is and why they should care about what you are talking about.

Put yourself in their shoes or seats and think about their levels of understanding about the topic. Is there reason for them to have any positive or negative connotations that you should consider? Why would they be interested in your topic? Does it impact them in some way? How can you seek to engage them in dialogue?

Step 1 Step 2

DON'T BE "THAT GUY"

Have you ever been stuck talking with someone at an event who only wants to talk about themselves? Maybe they were so focused on telling you all about themselves that they never asked you a single question. In those cases, what's happening isn't dialogue, it's a "tell," as in "let me tell you all about me."

In this scenario, the speaker is not interested in getting to know the listener at all, and it's a real communication turn-off. You can avoid this situation by considering your audience, their possible experiences, and what might be important (or unimportant) to them. Look for ways to engage them before they disengage with you.

To do this, it could be helpful to shift your perspective to consider how your audience will perceive you and your messages. Put yourself in their shoes or seats for a moment. This helps to ensure you communicate in the right direction. Otherwise, you run the risk of not only not engaging your audience but in possibly losing their support altogether.

In his long-revered book, *How to Win Friends and Influence People*, Dale Carnegie wrote, "When dealing with people, let us remember we are not dealing with creatures of logic. We are dealing with creatures of emotion, creatures bristling with prejudices, and motivated by pride and vanity." While not a wholly flattering summary of human behavior, they are good reminders to consider before seeking to capture someone else's attention.

SEEK TO UNDERSTAND YOUR AUDIENCE

The most important advice we can give to you here is don't assume you know what makes your audience tick. Assumptions about audiences are almost always wrong or riddled with critical errors. So get out there and listen. If you can't talk directly to your target audience, look for other options to understand them. Look for professional associations, nonprofit groups, social media accounts, publications, press releases, presentations, and other material to gain insight into your audience's goals and priorities. You also want to understand their specific language and their terminology to incorporate and reflect what you've heard. In other words, listen to learn and gain empathy for their experiences.

To make sure that you speak in a way that engages your audience, start by asking a few key questions:

1. **Who are they?** First, identify the audiences you want to connect with. It's typical to have multiple audiences, but you may want to pair different messages with different audiences. Name the groups you want to engage with as specifically as you can, for example are they families with

young children, elected officials who influence your funding, homeowners in a certain area, commercial fishermen, consumers making purchasing decisions, farmland owners in a specific watershed, and so on.

2. **What do you want them to do?** Be very clear about what your "call to action" is and provide a clear roadmap for how they can act. Consider what "success" looks like for you. Is it merely raising awareness around an issue, or do you want people to do something? For example, do you want them to start or stop a particular action, influence the behavior of others, or support your work financially?
3. **Why should they care?** We all need to get out of our own heads and into our audiences' heads so that we're not telling them what we think is interesting, yet rather what *they* might think is interesting. Look for the overlaps in what you want them to do and why they should care. In the case of the farmers in the example above, they cared about things like how building a wetland could help manage water storage on their lands, support livestock health, and what funding programs supported their specific needs.
4. **What motivates them?** Understanding what motivates your audience is different than why they should care, since this question is focused on who or what influences their decisions. For example, we found the biggest motivator for having farmers create wetlands on their land was knowing another farmer who had been through the process. That wasn't why they should care about a restoration project; it was instead one of the most effective paths to action. Knowing that peer-to-peer conversations are so valuable, we decided to tape several video interviews with farmers, farmland owners, and extension agents talking

about their experience. Would your audience be motivated by a rebate or cost-share program, peer pressure, perceptions of others, sense of community, or leaving future generations with a healthier environment?

5. **Who do they trust?** Lastly, consider who your audience trusts enough to influence their behavior. Ask questions like where else are they getting information about, or related to, your topic; are they looking online for information or having conversations within their communities; or are you and your organization already known and respected by your target audience? If not, consider working with individuals or groups they already know and trust that would share or support your efforts. Working with an existing "trusted messenger" can greatly accelerate progress.

UNDERSTANDING YOUR AUDIENCE

This chapter began with a quote from author Meredith Hill, "When you speak to everyone, you speak to no one." Audiences are rarely homogenous, so you need to break down what different sub-audiences care about. Your audience could very well include people from diverse age ranges, educational backgrounds, lifestyles, political views, income levels, geographic regions, prior knowledge of your topic, and so on. As Dale Carnegie alluded to, that means you have diverse motivations, biases, egos, and more to navigate around and appeal to.

We often develop what we term "user personas" to help us understand our various sub-audiences. User personas are tools that help us understand the range of people we are trying to connect with and provide a framework for how we might communicate with them.

Developing user personas helps us identify succinct, key messages that will resonate with specific audiences. The value in this exercise is not about describing a specific individual; rather, it is in characterizing a category of the larger audience. Please note that this does not mean stereotyping any categories. The process should be a genuine attempt to understand how they might feel about what you are doing or asking them to do. We typically develop several user personas during the strategic communication planning phase to ensure we have characterized most of the target audience. Then we refer to these as we develop campaigns, key messages, and associated materials.

For example, here are two personas for a hypothetical climate change community engagement project near Baltimore, Maryland.

Persona: Suburban Susanna	
Community	Howard County (suburb of Baltimore)
Age	38
Profession	Small business accountant
Lifestyle	Married, two children under age ten. Very involved in children's school activities and community health issues. She and her husband own a house in the suburbs of Baltimore.
Motivations and Triggers	Susanna and her family chose to live where they have access to local, fresh, organic produce and meats and outdoor recreational opportunities. She supports environmental initiatives, particularly those that have an immediate impact on her family. Flash floods have become a recurring danger in her community.

Trusted Sources	Susanna trusts news and information shared by her peers. She subscribes to the Washington Post, Baltimore Sun, and her local county paper.
Their Questions	How will climate change impact her neighborhood? What about home values in the long term? What are the human health implications of climate change around Baltimore? What can the city and the county do to minimize impacts? What can she do as an individual to help?

Persona: Leo the Advocate	
Geography	Downtown Baltimore
Age	63
Profession	Community organizer with a housing non-profit
Lifestyle	Leo is very engaged with his church. He does not have high trust in "government," although he has worked closely with the county on housing projects. He has a large extended family, many of whom live within the same community. He is an active member of a locally based non-profit organization focused on environmental justice.
Motivations and Triggers	Motivated to address housing inequalities around the city. Very vocal about these issues, public transportation, and healthcare services.
Trusted Sources	Leo trusts his peers and church community for information. He receives news and updates from his volunteer network through email and social media. He watches local news.
Their Questions	Is his community more vulnerable to climate impacts than surrounding areas? How will those impacts stress the existing inequalities around community services? What is the city doing to protect them?

If you aren't sure how to start developing your own user personas, consider talking with several stakeholders and asking them how they feel. You might include people who have experience in the issue you are talking about, people who will be impacted by the issue, or local leaders who understand the community. The resulting personas can then be used as a guide for gauging your messages. Are your messages reflective of the diversity that exists around the issue? Does your communication consider their lifestyle or motivations? Do your messages address their questions?

DEFINING THE NEEDED ACTION

Establishing environmental goals is an important step for any program, whether it is trying to reach a specific habitat restoration goal, air or water quality level, completion of infrastructure projects, or number of people participating in a program. Goals keep the work focused on a specific end point. Environmental goals, on their own, are rarely motivational selling points for others.

Earlier in the book we talked about a project we worked on to encourage more farmers to create or restore wetlands on their lands. EPA had identified farmers as a specific audience because they had a goal of restoring eighty-five thousand acres of wetlands across the Chesapeake Bay watershed. Because farmland owners typically own more acres than a typical homeowner and have conditions to support a wetland, almost all the restoration work was expected to occur on farmland. The math works in terms of a gross level assessment of where to find that many acres, but asking a farmer to permanently convert acreage into a wetland can be an uphill battle. It also isn't one where the audience is looking for this solution.

Loblolly Pine
Red Oak
Bald Eagle
Barn Swallow
Dragonfly
Monarch Butterfly
Snail
Ruby-Throated Hummingbird
Common Milkweed
Swamp Rose
Jewelweed
Spicebush
Buttonbush
Snowy Egret
Cattails
Water Striders
Mallard
Virginia Rail
American Black Duck
Spotted Turtle
Southern Leopard Frog
Great Blue Lobelia

So how do you get to know an audience like farmers across a six-state region? You go to a lot of meetings, make a lot of calls, and do a lot of listening. Farmers, farmland owners, technical assistance providers, and others understand what drives their own personal business decisions, what converting land means to their bottom line, what factors are involved in creating wetlands, and more. We really wanted to understand farmers, farming communities, and how a wetland might work for them, as well as why it might not.

What we found was that nearly everyone we spoke to was happily surprised someone wanted their input. So many programs had been developed *for* farmers but not *with* farmers. As we mentioned in the introduction, an interview with one farmer captured the essence of what environmentalists had been missing: "Stop trying to sell me on the ecological benefits of wetlands. Sell me on how a wetland would work for me." In other words, environmentalists had been communicating in the wrong direction, just like Briar Goldberg had observed. The goal of restoring wetlands on farmlands also missed the selling point of how farmers could benefit from the restoration programs.

Once you have put some thought into who your audiences are and what makes them tick, the fun part begins. How do you develop messages that really speak to them and accomplish your goals? Defining your call to action (CTA) is essential. What do you want people to do with the information you are giving them?

In the example above, there had not been a clear CTA for farmland owners related to wetland restoration. Our work defined the CTA as having the landowner get matched with the technical expertise and financial resources in support of their specific property decisions. Making these local connections facilitated participation in wetland restoration programs and helped educate landowners about the range of available options.

MESSAGES THAT RESONATE

The word "resonate" means to have particular meaning or importance to someone; to affect or appeal to someone in a personal or emotional way. Our goal for you is to help you frame messages that will connect with your audiences in ways that move them toward what you define as "success."

If you are not familiar with Frank Luntz and his work, maybe you should be. Luntz literally wrote the book on *Words That Work: It's Not What You Say, It's What People Hear.* Pay particular attention to his subtitle, because it's so true.

Luntz is a controversial figure, responsible for some of the most divisive campaigns in recent history, including working with Newt Gingrich to develop the "Contract with America" and replacing the term "estate tax" with "death tax." We do not honor his work but realize that it offers valuable lessons for environmental communication.

Before we get deeper into this section, we want to emphasize that partisan splits on environmental issues have been documented through public opinion polls. Data proves this point time and time again. However, this does not mean that we cannot find common ground and language. The words we use can either help pull us together or split us further apart.

None of Luntz's work has had the long-lasting impact on environmental protections as his advice to George W. Bush and other Republican leaders in the early 2000s to scrutinize the lack of scientific certainty around climate change and to use the term "climate change" instead of the more ominous "global warming" phrase. His hope was to sway public opinion away from action. We should note this approach ignores that the two terms are not interchangeable as they refer to different phenomena. Global warming is the process by which greenhouse gases build up in Earth's atmosphere and cause our planet to warm. Climate change is the resulting cascade of changes that is caused by global warming. It is also interesting to note that the term "climate change" has since become broadly embraced by climate scientists and advocates, perhaps because the public has evolved in their understanding of the issue.

Definitions aside, his approach gained traction. Luntz's work led to a highly partisan split over the issue. The Republican and Democratic parties began to move farther apart in the mid-2000s than they had been before (Resources for the Future, 2020). Luntz's understanding of how different words would resonate with voters over others was only one of the many assaults against taking climate change action, but it was a particularly insightful one.

In addition to financial ramifications for the fossil fuel industry, part of this success was due to confirmation bias. Many in the public do not want to believe that the planet and people are in danger from warming temperatures, especially due to their own actions (Leiserowitz, 2007; Lorenzonia et al. 2006). That makes them very receptive to someone, anyone, telling them there is nothing to worry about.

Confirmation bias, where you seek out information to confirm what you believe, is very real. The problem, of course, was that no credible scientists were, or are, debating the facts around climate change. Luntz's work helped shift the conversation from the fact that global warming was demonstrably happening to the uncertainty in the computer models projecting expected climate changes.

Scientists got caught in the trap of defending why uncertainty exists in complicated models when Americans accept uncertainty in every other aspect of their lives, including weather forecasts, food security, insurance rates, and investments, rather than focusing on the larger facts and the need to act. The challenge moving forward in a divided country where disinformation is now rampant is to stay focused on the long-term goals, understand our audiences better, develop strategic messages that resonate, and don't take the conversation shifting bait.

HOPE VERSUS FEAR

Jane Goodall is one of those rare individuals who is both a gifted scientist and communicator. In May 2021, we had an opportunity to hear her speak during a book launch event for Peter Wohlleben's *The Heartbeat of Trees: Embracing Our Ancient Bond with Forests and Nature* book launch. Goodall famously conducted pioneering research on chimpanzees in

Tanzania, and perhaps because of her primate field studies, she understands people pretty well too.

She spoke about the importance of listening and storytelling skills when trying to reach others. Paraphrasing Goodall's comments, she urged environmentalists to talk to people as individuals, present facts fairly, engage them in memorable stories, and resist the urge to issue blame. All these techniques provide foundations for people to understand each other and possibly have a change of mind.

Her words reminded us that from our own experience, we have not seen people change their minds after being yelled at or pushed into a corner. Blame and finger pointing usually builds walls, not bridges. While it might feel great at the time, it probably won't attract more people to support your goals. It could shore up existing support without widening the base.

Goodall reminded the environmentalists in the audience that we should not be surprised doom and gloom doesn't sell.

"People thrive on hope," she reminded us all. "Without hope, what's the point in even trying?" Doom overwhelms people, including the scientists who have been sounding the alarm on climate change for decades and for that carried around a tremendous communication burden.

Communicating hope includes identifying possible solutions to overcome environmental degradation. Providing tangible options for solutions not only helps people understand how their actions and larger collective action could make a difference in addressing environmental issues, it effectively focuses the conversation on "how" we can tackle it instead of "if" we should even try.

Words are tools to communicate and, as with other tools, can be used with proficiency to create works of art or used clumsily and inflict long-lasting harm. The lessons we've learned are broadly applicable to the range of environmental issues, from climate change to very local level projects.

EFFECTIVE MESSAGING DOS

Frame your messages around values that will resonate with your audience, because as Luntz reminds us, it isn't about what you say, it's about what your audiences hear. The key is to understand what themes and solutions resonate with your audiences and finding ways to fit your goals into those themes.

Here are a few of our suggestions for message framing.

Instead of this	Use this framing	Why this works
Regulations	Protections	Regulations and protections can be flip sides of the same coins, but where the mere mention of new or expanded regulation triggers a negative response in some, the word "protection" triggers a more positive response. It is especially effective to connect environmental protections to human health, community health, and character of place for broader support.

Instead of this	Use this framing	Why this works
Blame	Responsibility	As Brené Brown says, "Blame is one of the reasons we miss our opportunities for empathy" (2015). Finger pointing creates an "us versus them" situation, and while that *can* be an effective motivating tactic, it will quickly put someone else on the defense. Once defensive armor goes up, it's nearly impossible to engage and listen or be heard. Instead, consider framing issues in terms of "we all need to do our part" to be a good citizen. Encouraging personal and collective responsibility is a less threatening way to begin conversations when you seek behavior changes because it can build a bridge instead of setting one on fire.
Everything is awful	Offer possible solutions	No one wants to jump on a sinking ship, even if we live on that ship. In other words, hopelessness is not a motivator. Offer possible solutions framed at the individual or community-level scale that your audience can address. The human spirt is one of ingenuity, so use science to inspire hope. Case studies that highlight success stories are another way to provide hope by showing how action has worked in the past.
Single species/habitat focus	Interconnectivity	Most people can relate to how systems are interrelated, and the health of one depends on another. An example might be focusing on a single species, like a charismatic megafauna (e.g. polar bear floating on ice or a spotted owl) that audiences may have no connection to and may ultimately turn against.

Instead of this	Use this framing	Why this works
Scientific experts say	Show the data	Even though scientists are largely viewed as highly credible, framing messages around what they say can result in an "us against them" mentality. This might happen if people perceive those particular scientists in a negative light or if they feel they are being talked down to. Instead, show the data and put it into context for your audience. For example, "As you can see, wetlands now only occupy a small fraction of the acreage they used to."
Technical processes	Use metaphors and equivalencies	Simplify how things work by using metaphors that your audience can relate to. For example, wetlands act as nature's kidneys to filter out pollutants, or our atmosphere functions like a heat-trapping blanket and the more greenhouse gases that are emitted, the more heat is trapped.
Directly rebutting disinformation	Stay focused on data and outcomes	Anyone speaking about environmental issues is likely to encounter someone who just wants to disrupt the conversation, sometimes by interjecting talking points not grounded in reality. Instead of repeating disinformation meant to derail, emphasize the values connected to your work. For example, emphasize that your work uses credible data and will result in a healthier community, not only for current generations, but for future ones as well.

GOING FOR THE GOALS

The US Environmental Protection Agency (EPA) coordinates the Chesapeake Bay Program (CBP), which is a large restoration effort that includes seven jurisdictions and a multitude of federal, state, and local government as well as non-profit and academic partners. The CBP and its partners seek to restore the Chesapeake Bay as defined by specific goals and thirty-one outcomes.

Those outcomes include restoring oysters, blue crabs, underwater grass, wetlands, tree canopy, riparian forest buffers, and many more objectives. Given the scope of the effort and the range of outcomes sought, it's no wonder the amount of material and its complexity can intimidate some people. Additionally, those themes were not always capturing the attention of local government staff, who are responsible for a myriad of decisions that directly impact goal attainment. For example, if you worked within a local government office, restoring wetlands or planting trees might not feel like your highest priorities when compared against budgets, schools, roads, human health, and other issues.

To better engage local government and local elected officials, our firm, Green Fin Studio, worked with the EPA to develop educational materials that connect the CBP outcomes to local government priorities. Local government staff had previously been surveyed to identify what their priorities were. The short list of priorities identified in that process were: economic development, public health and safety, infrastructure maintenance and finance, and education. We took that list and reviewed over three hundred primary source materials that made connections between environmental restoration and protection and those local government priorities. Then we took all those findings and created a series of educational modules for local government staff that explained those connections: How protecting forests and wetlands can save hundreds of thousands of dollars in storm-water management, how property values increase with proximity to open space, that investing in green jobs provides a resilient and future-focused workforce, that the health of many businesses relies upon clean water, and many more benefits.

We presented the information as succinctly and visually as possible. Here is an example graphic from the modules that conveys the benefits of trees and wetlands in reducing stormwater runoff.

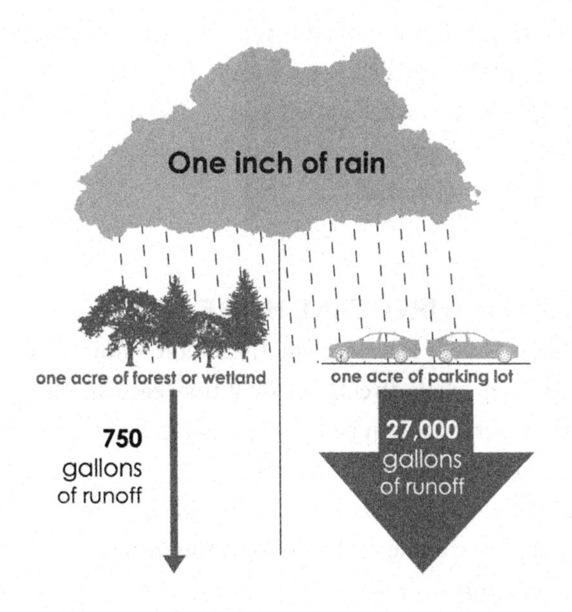

In addition to making the connections between local government priorities and CBP goals, we also provided links to technical and financial resources that support local programs. By providing the "why" restoration and protection actions are important along with information on "how" localities can find needed assistance, the modules provide a roadmap that local staff can use to close the gaps on goal attainment.

The set of modules we developed is collectively termed "A Local Government Guide to the Chesapeake Bay" and can be found on the Chesapeake Bay Program website.

Did the modules connect with their intended audiences? Did they ever! After reviewing the modules, one local government leader said that in her twenty-five years of experience in working with the CBP, this was the most valuable product she had ever seen. Because we took the time to connect the messages to the target audience, the modules are being used by local government staff around the sixty-four thousand square mile watershed.

CHAPTER THREE TAKE HOME TIPS

1. Identify your audience and then get to know them so that you can speak directly to what they care about.
2. User personas can be a useful tool in characterizing the diversity within your audience.
3. Define your call to action by identifying what you want your audience to do with the information you are providing.
4. Stay on course and focused on your message and goals and don't allow others to shift the conversation to fit their own agenda.
5. Whenever possible, include solutions-focused and scale-appropriate options for your audiences. Without that, doom and gloom kill hope and your audiences will be overwhelmed.

6. Develop selling points around your programmatic goals. Effective environmental communication is about finding ways to connect with your audience in support of your goals.
7. Frame your messages in ways that draw people in rather than creating more division.

RESOURCES

1. Visit the COMPASS website at: CompassSciComm.org and try out their Message Box tool to develop targeted communications.
2. Visit Randy Olson's website, the Narrative Gym, at: NarrativeGym.com to learn from his experience in developing narratives around the and, but, therefore (ABT) model.

CHAPTER FOUR

JUST SAY NO TO JARGON

"I think we invent jargon because it saves time talking to one-another."

—JOHN MAYNARD SMITH

In previous chapters, we've spoken about audience and messaging and the importance of establishing each when developing your communications. On the journey to effective communications, establishing who your audience is (or audiences are) and your messaging are critical to effective and inclusive communication.

However, once we've established our audience and message, we need to make sure the language we use is understandable to the people we are speaking to. Why is this essential? Because making science relevant and accessible is necessary for continued public engagement and investments into research and environmental action. That's right, there's no avoiding it, we're going to have the talk about jargon! You knew it was coming. After all, this is a book that references science communication. You're just lucky we didn't hit you with it right out of the gate. Don't worry, we will try and be brief.

Jargon is kryptonite to effective communication. Whoops—I think a jargon bomb was just dropped. It was assumed that you are familiar with Superman lore when we used the term "kryptonite." Let's explain—Superman is a comic book superhero who is invincible to anything except an alien substance called kryptonite which causes him to lose all of his superpowers. Anyway, you can have done your homework in terms of identifying your audiences and developed a messaging strategy that hits them right in the motivators, but if you are using jargon at any point in the process, it's likely to all come crashing down.

By the way, we never use the phrase "dumb things down" when we talk about making messaging broadly understandable. Frankly that's insulting to the speaker and the audience. If someone believes making their work understandable and relevant to others is dumb, why are they even engaged in that work? And all audiences can't be expected to know the secret language of scientists. Needing to explain complex topics in terms they can understand doesn't make them dumb.

WHAT IS JARGON?

While most jargon is easy to recognize, let's take a look at why jargon exists. To control the use of jargon, it can be helpful to better understand it. Jargon is not specific to environmental science. It exists in all professions. Have you ever been to see your accountant and she starts dropping terms like accruals or depreciation, and while you're still puzzling over these terms, she's already on to another topic? Before you know it, you are just kind of nodding your head rather than admitting you are completely lost.

Or you go to your mechanic because your car is having troubles, and while he's talking about ignition coils and CV joints, you're thinking, "Well, this sounds pretty complicated, so I guess that's why it's costing me thousands of dollars to get it fixed." Even if you are vaguely familiar with the terms, it can be like using the rusty French you learned back in high school trying to understand someone from Paris.

jargon | jar · gon | jär-gən | noun

1: the technical terminology or characteristic idiom of a special activity or group
2: obscure and often pretentious language marked by circumlocutions and long words

The Merriam-Webster dictionary defines jargon as "the technical terminology or characteristic idiom of a special activity or group," and "obscure and often pretentious language marked by circumlocutions and long words." By the way, according to the Merriam-Webster dictionary, circumlocution means "the use of an unnecessarily large number of words to express an idea."

Bottom line, jargon is specific to a particular group. It is obscure and pretentious, and when you look up the definition, you must look up words in the definition. It isn't good and not suggestive that jargon is the way to clear and understandable communication.

Basically, jargon is the language of a specific profession. In all honesty, it is necessary for effective communication within that profession. If, instead of using the word accruals accountants instead said, "The list of expenses that have not been paid," things would tend to get a little wordy around the office. If they did the same for all other accounting terms, communication among colleagues would grind to a halt. So, jargon is a needed component for efficient communication among people in the same profession or those who are "inside the tent." This makes sense and lines up perfectly with the first part of Webster's definition. Now let's look at the second part where the words "obscure" and "pretentious" are used. This brings to light the darker side of jargon.

THE SECRET HANDSHAKE

Obscure and pretentious are not very friendly words. This gets to the idea that jargon can be used as sort of a litmus test to judge if the person you are communicating with is "in the know." In this way, it is a bit of a secret handshake to determine if someone is in the club (or in the tent). If you are in the know, you feel accepted because you can take part in the discussion. If you aren't, then you can feel excluded and even talked down to.

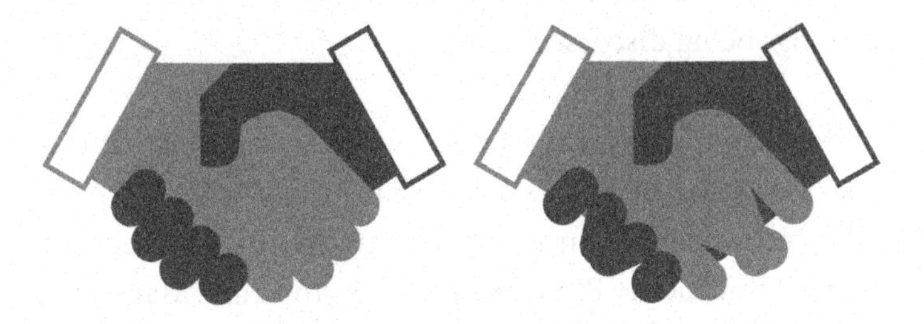

A recent study found that pervasive use of jargon made people feel less interested in science (Hillary et al., 2020). In the study, two groups of people were given science related articles. In the first group jargon was used throughout the articles, and in the second jargon was removed and replaced with easier to understand terms with identical meaning. The groups were then asked a series of questions about how easy the articles were to read and their thoughts about science.

Unsurprisingly, most of the people in the jargon group found the articles difficult to read. What's more, they also expressed they weren't good at science and didn't want to learn more about it. Interestingly, the researchers provided definitions for the jargon for half of the individuals in the jargon group, and this had no effect on the result. They still didn't understand the articles and still had negative feelings about science. The people in the non-jargon group had the opposite responses, indicating they understood the articles and had a good grasp of science.

It gets worse, though. Another study on the same individuals found that **use of jargon actually led to disbelief in**

the science (Bullock et al., 2019). Since the jargon made the reading unpleasant, the readers would form negative opinions about the work and become resistant to the scientific findings being discussed.

Perhaps even more surprising is the recent finding that the use of jargon by scientists may be harming science. The *New York Times* reported on an article in the journal Proceedings of the Royal Society B (Kornei, 2021; Martinez and Mammola, 2021). The abstracts of over twenty-one thousand scientific articles about cave science were analyzed for jargon words and phrases. To identify jargon, the text in each abstract was compared to a list of about one thousand five hundred cave science jargon words that the authors assembled from a review of cave science texts and other publications. They compared the proportion of jargon words in each abstract to the number of times that paper was cited by other authors. They found that papers with a higher amount of jargon in their abstracts were cited less often by other scientists.

This has serious implications for science. If scientists are not reading their peers' work not because of the merit of that work but simply because there is too much jargon, then useful information is not being shared and science is not advancing as it should. Using information from scientific literature to support and inform your findings is a critical part of how science advances. If jargon is preventing this from happening, it is cause for concern.

In the same *Times* article, another study is discussed that examined the abstracts of almost twenty thousand proposals to the National Science Foundation (NSF) (Markowitz,

2019). The relationship between the use of jargon and funding awarded was examined. The finding suggested that NSF awarded more money to proposals whose abstracts contained more jargon. This pattern flies in the face of NSF's call for scientists to communicate in a clearer manner (National Science Foundation, 2021). Perhaps the scientists who review these funding requests are still beholding to the secret handshake and are favoring those who are inside the tent.

This is not to say that everyone who uses jargon is trying to make the person who doesn't understand the jargon feel excluded. In most cases they are not. In most cases, they are simply using the efficient language of their profession and have been using it for so long that they don't even think about it. However, when speaking to folks outside the tent, they need to think about the language they use. By doing so, they are not only being a better communicator, but they are also being more *inclusive.*

A FRIENDLY APPROACH

One field of science that has more jargon than there are fish in the ocean is, well, fisheries science. With terms like maximum sustainable yield, and recruitment, and bycatch, you can almost see the tent flaps closing when you get into a conversation with a fisheries scientist.

We worked on a project with the New England Fishery Management Council as they were in the process of evaluating a new way of managing fish species off the coast of New England. Our role was to develop a series of communication and outreach products to help them engage with their stakeholders about a more holistic approach to fisheries management, Ecosystem Based Fishery Management or EBFM.

Imagine trying to manage wild populations of fish species in the open ocean (fish have absolutely no respect for borders or boundaries) that are subject to vagaries of weather and climate and whatever else Mother Nature can throw their way on top of the man-made issues of pollution and climate change. Meanwhile, fishermen want to make a living, managers are trying to keep enough fish in the ocean so there are more to catch next year, and the public wants to keep the ocean healthy while still being able to get a bargain price on fish sticks at the supermarket. This is of course an oversimplification, but the bottom line is that a lot of people's livelihoods depend on the continued health of the Atlantic fishery. If fish populations decline, there can be finger pointing about who is responsible. Clear communication about how managers aim to maintain the health of the fishery is vitally important. So, no pressure for us!

Back to our story... We've established there are many jargon terms in fisheries' science. However, because the livelihoods of fishermen depend on the decisions of fishery managers and managers base their decisions on the findings of scientists, everyone is in on the jargon. The interaction between fishermen, managers, and scientists has been going on so long that everyone is inside the tent. Although, what happens when you introduce a new style of fishery management? Brand new jargon appears.

This is a potentially combustible situation. We know that fishermen are concerned about making a living and have reason to be suspicious of any attempt to change a management system that, while not perfect, is understood by them. Add in the findings from Bullock and team on how people, when faced with jargon, may disbelieve the science it is associated with it. This does not bode well for fishermen being receptive to this new form of management.

How do you develop shared understanding so that everyone involved can communicate and engage effectively about this new form of management? One solution we identified for outreach materials was a glossary of terms (a.k.a. jargon) associated with EBFM. However, this was not a typical glossary, which is generally just a list of definitions. Our glossary was a visual one with illustrations to help support the definitions. The idea was that this would be a "friendlier" document. It is engaging to look at, which may help ease any subconscious distrust someone may have when encountering words or phrases that they consider to be jargon.

New England Fishery Management Council

NEFMC Glossary of Terms

Algae
A group of simple photosynthetic organisms that are typically aquatic. Algae can range from single-celled organisms to seaweed.

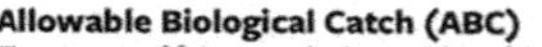

Allowable Biological Catch (ABC)
The amount of fish, or catch, that may be safely harvested from a stock or stock complex. It is set by the Council through its Scientific and Statistical Committee.

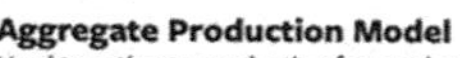

Aggregate Production Model
Used to estimate production for stock complexes. These models are informed by catch and biomass or abundance estimates for the stock complexes. They do not directly account for the size or age of fish, but can be used to estimate maximum sustainable yield (MSY).

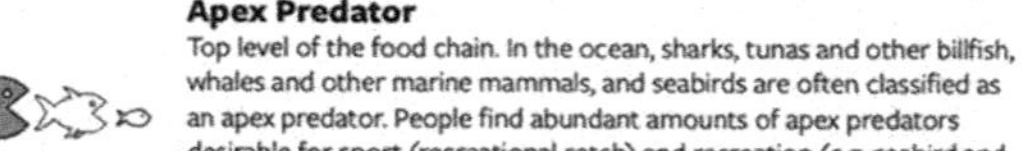

Apex Predator
Top level of the food chain. In the ocean, sharks, tunas and other billfish, whales and other marine mammals, and seabirds are often classified as an apex predator. People find abundant amounts of apex predators desirable for sport (recreational catch) and recreation (e.g. seabird and whale watching). Because they catch many species of fish and do not generally serve as prey in the oceans (although there are infrequent exceptions), humans are also considered to be apex predators in an ecosystem sense.

Benthic
Refers to the bottom habitat of the ocean and the animals that live there. For example, haddock and lobsters live on the bottom of the ocean and are therefore benthic species. Benthic species typically eat organisms buried in or on the seafloor, such as worms and mollusks, species that are considered as 'Benthos'.

- *Related terms - demersal, pelagic*

Biomass
The total weight of living matter, generally measured within a specific area or volume. Biomass is usually calculated by species, stock, or other grouping. For example, the total biomass of cod or the total biomass.

Bycatch
Fish and/or other marine creatures caught by gear in addition to the target species of that gear and discarded, either dead or alive. Bycatch is often comprised of unmarketable or illegal fish, but also includes other animals such as dolphins, whales, sea turtles, and seabirds that become hooked or entangled in fishing gear.

Climate
Refers to the long-term minimums, averages, and maximums of temperature and precipitation that are characteristic of a particular region or area of water. This is different from weather which refers to the conditions of temperature and precipitation experienced on a day-to-day basis. In the ocean, we track trends in climate as averages of temperature, pH (acidity), salinity, and currents.

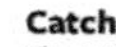

Catch
The total number of fish caught in a fishery in a given period of time. Catch is given in either weight or number of fish and may include landings, unreported landings, discards, and incidental deaths. Note that catch, harvest, and landings have different definitions.

Obviously, a visual glossary was only one facet in our overall approach to developing communication materials for this project. We strove to use non-jargon terms in presentations and brochures; everything was highly visual to make it more engaging and inviting, and for one brochure we created audience specific versions to make it more relatable to these audiences. All of these materials had a clear invitation to the reader that their input on this potential new form of management was not only desired, but it was critical to the process. In other words, every effort was made to be inclusive and invite people into the tent.

BUT DON'T OVERSIMPLIFY...

One of our science communication heroes is Dave's Master's Thesis advisor, Dr. Walter Boynton. Boynton has been researching the Chesapeake Bay for decades and has a reputation for being able to explain how the Bay "works" to anyone; a skill recognized by journalists around the Chesapeake region looking for an explanation about the health of the Bay and what can be done to fix it.

Through Boynton, Dave gained the understanding that just because a topic is complex, the way you tell people about it doesn't have to be. From the way he spoke during presentations to the attention he gave to how graphs and figures were developed, he truly had a way of engaging with audiences of all backgrounds. We recently spoke with Boynton about his approach to communications to audiences with a spectrum of technical backgrounds and his skills as a communicator. Boynton admits this wasn't always the case. He told a story about how, when he was a newly minted PhD, he became acutely aware of the gap between what he was saying and what others heard.

Many years ago, at the beginning of his career, Boynton was running experiments on the eastern shore of Maryland. His project required measuring phytoplankton in the waters of Chincoteague Bay. Phytoplankton are floating, marine algae in the water and are essentially not visible to the naked eye. Phytoplankton are plant-like in that they can convert sunlight into energy. We should also note that they are the basis of the food chain—without them, marine ecosystems would collapse. Boynton's experiments occurred over several weekends one summer and always involved a flurry of activity with him lugging buckets of seawater back and forth between the water's edge and a small shed where he was running his experiments.

After several weekends of this, one of the locals who had been observing these strange goings-on finally asked him, "Hey, what are you doing with all those buckets of water?"

Boynton was thrilled the person was asking about his work, so he replied, "I'm here studying the phytoplankton in the water."

The gentleman then asked the obvious question, "What are phytoplankton?"

Boynton eagerly said, "Oh, phytoplankton are plants, and they live in the water." *This was going great,* he thought. *The locals are interested and engaged in science.*

But the man quickly shot back, "Well, I've lived here my whole life and have never seen any plants in that water."

Boynton nodded his head excitedly and explained, "Well, yes, that's because they are invisible!"

No sooner were the words out of his mouth when he realized he may have just confirmed suspicions of insanity. The gentleman politely nodded but stopped asking Boynton questions. What else could explain the actions of a man who returned to the same spot, weekend after weekend, to study "invisible" plants?

This was a "light bulb" moment for Boynton. In trying to correct his use of jargon, he had gone too far in the other direction and oversimplified his explanation. Unfortunately, there isn't always a one-to-one replacement of a jargon word with a broadly understood non-jargon word. As we'll discuss, it can sometimes be a ten to one replacement.

Boynton never forgot his early career experience of explaining phytoplankton to a few interested bystanders. His scientific work went on to illuminate our understanding of how nitrogen, phosphorus, and sediment impact water quality. As we mentioned earlier, the public sees science's brand as "hope," but scientists themselves see it as "joy." Boynton is a much sought-after speaker for a variety of audiences because he's able to translate the hope that science offers while conveying the true joy of his work to others in a clear, engaging manner.

Breaking free from jargon takes practice. As we discussed above, eliminating jargon may mean you must use ten words where before just one would do. This may seem inefficient at first. However, the alternative of your audience not understanding what you are talking about is not efficient at all.

We present below an example from the marine ecology world where we explain a concept using all the jargon we need and then explaining it using no jargon.

Jargon

Hypoxia in Chesapeake Bay is exacerbated by eutrophication that causes phytoplankton blooms that fuel elevated benthic metabolism.

Non-Jargon

Low oxygen levels in Chesapeake Bay waters, which are harmful to the fish, crabs, and oysters that live there, are made worse by pollution washing off the land and out of wastewater plants. This pollution contains chemicals that fuel rapid growth of algae living in the water. When algae grow rapidly it is called a bloom, and when these blooms eventually die, they settle out of the water and land on the bottom of the Bay where they are eaten by bacteria. As these bacteria consume the algae, they also consume oxygen out of the water, which can cause low oxygen levels.

This illustrates the idea that the no-jargon approach uses far more words; nonetheless, we hope you'll agree, in the end it provides a much more understandable explanation.

When you are writing or preparing your presentation, think about the audience who you will be communicating with. Ask yourself if they will understand the words and phrases you are using. The American Geophysical Union (AGU) suggests scientists communicate at a ninth grade reading level. This helps ensure that what you are communicating will be understandable by as broad an audience as possible.

If your neighbors and family members wouldn't understand the words you are using, you are likely using jargon.

CHAPTER FOUR TAKE HOME TIPS

1. All professions use jargon, and it is necessary to a certain point for efficient communication among colleagues.
2. Jargon can unintentionally make others feel excluded when it is used by scientists or environmental professionals in explanations of complex topics to general audiences. Sometimes, however, jargon is an intentional "secret handshake" that lets people know who is in the club and who isn't.
3. Eliminating jargon will help make people interested in your messaging, while using it could make them biased against it.
4. Think about your audience when you are communicating. Are you using words they wouldn't use? Would your friends and family understand what you're saying? If not, consider explaining things more clearly.

RESOURCES

1. Use ScienceAndPublic.com, a free online de-jargonizer tool that instantly analyzes how accessible your writing is.
2. Pick up a copy of *If I Understood You, Would I Have This Look on My Face?: My Adventures in the Art and Science of Relating and Communicating* by Alan Alda for his encouragement and tips for scientists to improve their communication with non-technical audiences.

CHAPTER FIVE

THE SCIENCE OF STORY AND THE STORY OF SCIENCE

"Story, as it turns out, was crucial to our evolution—more so than opposable thumbs. Opposable thumbs let us hang on; story told us what to hang on to."

—LISA CRON

Humans have been telling each other stories since we sat around the fire in caves. Our brains are wired for it. Liz Neely, former director of the Story Collider, says areas of someone's brain light up on an MRI scan when they are being told a story. These include areas involved in movement, language processing, and emotion (Renken, 2020). Perhaps even more interesting is that when the brain waves of both the storyteller and the listener are monitored, the more the listener comprehends the story, the more their brainwaves mirror those of the teller. Neely suggests that listeners may keep thinking about a story, tell others about it, and therefore remember it better.

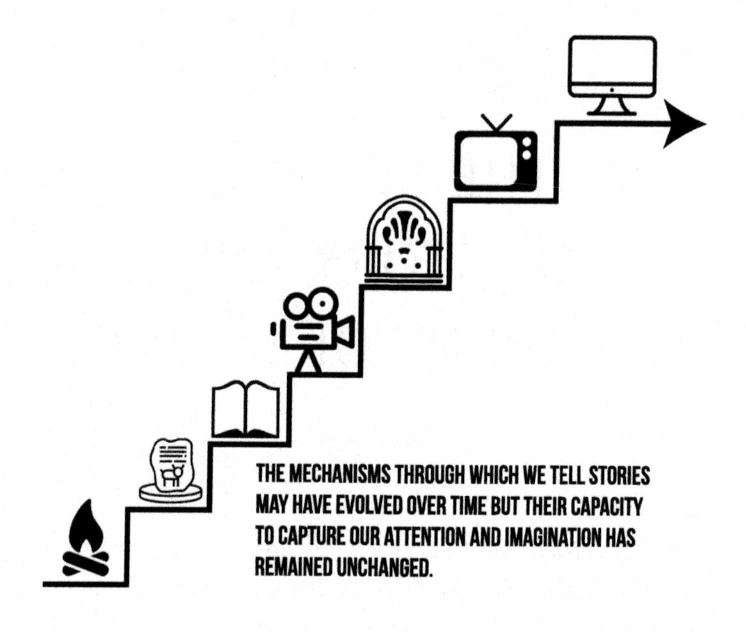

Neuroscience tells us that two small areas of our brains process language. Wernicke's area processes what we hear, and Broca's area helps us speak. These parts of your brain are very efficient at what they do, and they can be ruthless in what they choose to keep (memory) and ditch (forget immediately). Stories, however, engage all your brain in a way that's similar to you actually experiencing firsthand what you are hearing and commit it to memory.

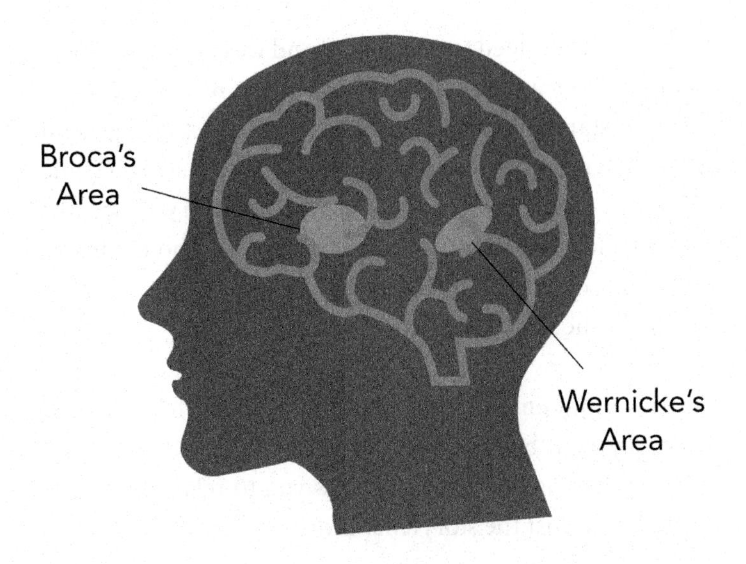

Think about that. As scientists we often think about data as our currency. Data defines reality for many of us, yet merely sharing our shiny, unbiased, glorious data with others doesn't necessarily make them understand or trust us. However, weaving narratives with that data can. And, given the universal appeal of stories, this approach may allow you to engage with a much broader audience than your subject matter might normally expect. For example, if your research involves the lifecycle of fruit flies, it might be tough to interest anyone except a fellow fruit fly scientist unless you can create rich storylines.

Dave was recently looking for something new to binge watch on Netflix (no judgment, please). A show that kept coming up in his recommendations was one about Formula One (F1) racing. Dave didn't pay any attention to the recommendation for a while. After all, he is not a racing fan and wasn't even sure what F1 was. But, after not finding anything else to watch, he decided to give it a try and was almost instantly hooked. Why are we telling you this, you might ask? Dave didn't instantly develop an interest in F1 or racing in general. He was, however, drawn in by the stories of the struggles and triumphs of the drivers and teams. The more he watched, the more he learned about who the drivers are, who the teams are, who routinely wins and who doesn't, and even a little bit about the rules of F1 racing.

Stories build empathy for the storyteller. When you feel empathy, your brain releases oxytocin, your body's natural stress-relieving hormone that tells you to relax. This cycle makes you trust the storyteller more.

If you aren't incorporating storytelling into your communications strategy, you are missing out on a powerful tool that will help you connect with your audiences. Science shows that once you start framing your messaging in the structure of a story, you've already primed your audience's brains to be turned on and tuned in.

So, all signs point to the importance of storytelling. But what does that mean exactly? Let's consider the factors that are common to all good stories—conflict, tension, and resolution. I think we can all agree that a story in which the hero loses at the end is not very satisfying. However, figuring out the problem and bringing it to resolution makes everyone happy.

Most scientific research and environmental campaigns are centered around trying to solve a problem or series of problems. Describing what those problems are, the obstacles to solving them, and then the solution that was found is a simple recipe for introducing narrative.

Let's consider an example from the space program. The National Aeronautics and Space Administration (NASA) wants to study Mars for signs of life, and the problem they need to solve is how to do it. Mars is far away and, with current technology, too risky for humans to make the trip. Bummer, but we're sensing a little tension here, so we're intrigued.

The NASA scientists think, "I know, we'll send a robot up there to do our exploring and studying for us."

Then they think, "But wait, how's a robot going to move around by itself on the rocky surface of Mars?" Ooooh, more tension.

Light bulb moment: "What if it isn't a robot but more of a remote-controlled car?"

Problem solved. Launch the rocket and make history.

Or, more clearly this time: NASA scientists wanted to explore Mars to look for signs of life. Unfortunately, Mars is so far away that current technology prohibits us from sending astronauts. A possible solution is to send a robot; however, the terrain would make that difficult. So NASA researchers developed a semi-autonomous rover that can handle the rough terrain. Launch the rocket, make history.

The previous paragraph was (apart from being an egregious over-simplification of the Mars rover program) an example of telling a story instead of just spewing out facts. The fact-spewing approach would have gone something like: NASA scientists, looking for signs of life on Mars, developed a semi-autonomous rover to study the planet. That statement is very direct and to the point. It is also completely forgettable.

The narrative approach works in the environmental world as well. However, in the environmental world (and the science world in general), we rarely completely solve a problem. Most often, we make incremental progress, and we need to convince others to be part of the story and contribute to that progress.

Environmental campaigns frequently ask their stakeholders to take up new behaviors or make adjustments to their property to help move the needle on littering or stormwater pollution or even energy usage. One of the hurdles these campaigns frequently encounter is that nobody wants to be the first to take action. In citizen A's mind, everyone else seems to be happy with the status quo, so why should they be the first to jump on board the change train? It really doesn't matter that they aren't the first, that others have already adopted new behaviors or made changes to their property. Citizen A only has their experience to go on, and that experience tells them by looking around at their friends and neighbors, they will be alone in this new activity.

This is where storytelling can be extremely powerful in the form of success stories. These are simple vignettes that profile an individual who has adopted the new behavior. They detail who the individual is, why they were interested in the new behavior, what problems they encountered (there's the tension!) and how they overcame them (resolution!), and how, in the end, they are happy they made the choice they did and are seeing benefits.

Why does this type of storytelling work in getting people to act? Because it normalizes the action. It helps Citizen A understand that other people are taking action and are happy that they did. The action is now normal and not unusual. If you're still in doubt as to the efficacy of success stories, they've been in use on TV and radio since the invention of these devices, only they're called commercials. While the narrative of most of these commercials is completely made up, they follow the same arc as a success story. The hero has a problem. The hero uses the product being sold to solve the problem. The hero is happier than anyone has a right to be. Success!

Why not learn from an industry that has been successfully convincing people to do things for decades and decades? Only we aren't trying to convince them to buy a product they may or may not need (let's be honest, they probably don't). We are trying to convince them to buy into taking action that benefits themselves and, ultimately, the planet.

The power of storytelling in effective communication is obviously not new. If you are reading this book, you've likely read others that make the same case. However, not many other authors make the case the way Randy Olson does, and he's created a strategy that can help simplify your attempts to create a narrative.

RANDY OLSON WANTS TO HELP SCIENTISTS SHARPEN THEIR MESSAGES

Olson isn't just any scientist. He earned a swoon-worthy academic pedigree and then one movie changed his professional trajectory and set him on a science communication crusade. In 1984, he graduated from Harvard with a PhD in evolutionary biology and went on to become a tenured marine biology professor at the University of New Hampshire in 1994.

What happened in 1993, just before gaining his tenureship, would change his life and career trajectory forever. In 1993, the movie *Jurassic Park* was released. It not only made box office records, it also became a cultural phenomenon. As a professor in evolutionary biology, Olson saw that scientists were missing something big. Scientific journals are filled with papers on paleontology and what life was like when dinosaurs roamed the earth. What got people to really care, though, was the power of films and narrative.

Within a year of *Jurassic Park*'s release, Olson was accepted into the film school at the University of Southern California (USC). He wanted to learn what Harvard and the larger scientific community were missing... connections. One of his professors at USC taught him that first, you must arouse the interest of your audience, get them listening to you, then begin to start giving them the substance of what you have to say. Hollywood was good at getting people to listen. Much better than PBS (with apologies to Sir David Attenborough and the rest of the crew) where the audiences were largely already among the "converted." They already cared about nature and conservation, which is why they were watching

PBS. However, those programs weren't converting new people to care or take action.

Olson hoped that film school could impart some of its magic on him and he could use the medium to deliver more compelling movies about issues he cared about, like environmental protections and ocean conservation. While he was studying film development, he came to realize how essential the narrative was. It couldn't just be interesting. PBS was interesting, at least to some viewers. The narrative had to follow certain rules. Olson began to find a pattern in successful narratives, from TV shows like *South Park* and historical works back to Aristotle that showed *tension* and *resolution* were essential ingredients in engaging storylines.

After years of trying to crack the code, he boiled his theory down to what he terms the ABT theory, consisting of "and, but, therefore." Since scientists have been trained to always "show their work," they tend to believe that complicated is better. So, regardless of who they are communicating with, they bombard the audience with data. Pick up a scientific journal or try and sit through sessions at a professional conference and you'll quickly see that simplicity and public engagement are not the goals. Those complicated, nuanced, heavily caveated messages are fine, even required, for peer-to-peer material. They aren't fine if your goal is to increase scientific literacy and appreciation in the general population. Enter the ABT story structure. As Olson explains in his book, *Houston, We Have a Narrative*, every story can be reduced to this formula.

Applying this framework to some real-life projects we recently worked on, it could look like:

> "Restoring wetlands protects water quality, AND there are multiple restoration resources available to landowners, BUT many of them find the restoration process complicated; THEREFORE, we have created an easy-to-use guide."

Or an even bigger, hairier communication issue to wrestle with:

> "Our climate is changing due to a buildup of greenhouse gases in our atmosphere AND the impacts on the environment are already occurring, BUT some people think it is a problem that won't affect us for decades; THEREFORE, we have conducted an analysis of weather data from the past century to show that change has already happened."

Olson believes the ABT narrative structure is essential in helping scientists distill their messages. Many scientists still push back, saying they cannot simplify their work into such a constrictive format. They don't have to, but unless they can make their work engaging and compelling, it becomes irrelevant to non-technical audiences.

The structure forces us to distill our messages into a simple phrase. Getting to simple isn't easy. Capturing the essential heart of your work means you may have to lose caveats, footnotes, or parts of your one hundred-plus slide deck of graphs and charts. But it's worth it if you want to connect with others.

Olson points out that this structure exists and works even when it isn't followed explicitly. One of the most well-known examples of this is the Trump campaign slogan, "Make America Great Again." This implies America was great and can be again, but it isn't currently great; therefore, you need to vote for me.

That narrative is of course riddled with, at best, flawed assumptions. But did it work? Yes. It was a simple story narrative that stuck.

SPEAK VISUALLY

So, telling a story is an important strategy for communicating with your audience. Part of being a good storyteller is being able to connect with your audience and help them understand the complexities of your narrative. This can be challenging for scientists and environmental communicators. Trying to weave a story while not glossing over complex topics and concepts can be difficult. As we discussed above, scientists lean toward the complicated in their communications, wanting to show that their conclusions are backed by data. Add to the fact that, in the environmental world, we are often dealing with large quantities and numbers that are on scales a lot of people have difficulty comprehending.

One trick we often use is to put large numbers or quantities in relative terms that people will have an easier time understanding. One of the most elegant examples of this is an explanation Dave's master's thesis advisor, Dr. Walter Boynton, used when describing the Chesapeake Bay.

The Chesapeake is North America's largest estuary. It is over two hundred miles long from its northern extent at the border of Maryland and Pennsylvania to where it meets the Atlantic Ocean at Cape Henry, Virginia.

An interesting fact about the Chesapeake is that it is incredibly shallow. The average depth is only about twenty-one feet deep over all the 4,500 square miles that it covers. This shallowness is a very important characteristic of the Chesapeake.

Boynton, who frequently gives talks about the Bay, often discusses how the Bay is so shallow. However, the idea that twenty-one feet isn't that deep is lost on a lot of audiences. In their defense, it sounds deep when compared to most backyard swimming pools. To help make the point that, given the size of the Bay, an average depth of twenty-one feet is shallow, Boynton gives a more "visual" description: If you took the 4,500 square miles of Chesapeake Bay and shrunk it down so it would fit on an 8.5 by 11 piece of paper, the average depth would be thinner than the paper.

This is an explanation that people can wrap their heads around. It takes an idea that is a bit difficult to conceptualize and puts it in terms that anyone with an even passing familiarity with office supplies can understand.

THIS EQUALS THAT

Another strategy to make large numbers more relatable is to use equivalencies. This technique is often used in science articles. For example, did you know that the United States emits about 11,243,562,000,000 pounds of CO_2 each year (USGS, 2019)? That's a really big number. That number is so big that it's a bit beyond comprehension. To put it into relatable terms, let's compare that weight to something we have a reasonable approximation of the same weight and that people are familiar with.

How about the Empire State Building (730,000,000 pounds)? Doing the math, the total amount of CO_2 emitted by the USA every year is equivalent to 15,402 Empire State Buildings, or ESBs for short. That's a lot of ESBs! I'm not sure that helps explain things, though, because while we know that 15,402 ESBs is a lot, it's still difficult to comprehend what that would look like.

So, we can either find a heavier equivalency or find a way to visualize 15,402 ESBs. Let's try both. Let's go really big on the equivalency—the Great Pyramid (estimated weight 11,500,000,000 pounds). Doing the math, the total amount of CO_2 emitted each year by the USA is equivalent to the weight of 978 Great Pyramids. Heavy! But let's not abandon our 15,402 ESBs. The base of the ESB occupies 79,288 square feet. Doing some more math, 15,402 ESBs would fill almost 44 square miles. That's enough to fill Manhattan, twice. Any way you look at it, the USA puts out a *lot* of CO_2.

THINKING VISUALLY AND THE POWER OF TED TALKS

You just can't beat good visuals. After all, have you seen Hans Rosling's presentation about big (in all senses of that word) data? Through a data visualization tool of his own design, Rosling would walk audiences through data, highlighting connections between such things as global health and wealth not normally visible through your average chart. Statistical formulas and p-values have their place; it's just not in presentations to non-technical audiences.

The TED stage provides a huge canvas for images to really have an impact. Whether your backdrop is as impressive as their screen sizes or not, graphics help convey your messages in ways that a thousand words could not.

Compelling graphics can overcome language and jargon barriers often present in science communication. They can transcend knowledge gaps. Images are more readily understood than data tables or even verbal explanations. Humans are wired for pictures. Take advantage of how accessible graphics are and think about the best way to convey information through maps, infographics, conceptual diagrams, and other forms of visual communication. If you need some help on how to get started with visualizing data, David McCandless has a great TED talk (see Resources) on the beauty of data visualization.

The collective phenomena of TED talks have changed public awareness, discourse, and action around many large issues. They successfully connect complex issues to non-technical audiences, an ideal in science communication. Hans Rosling's presentations (also see Resources) brought to life big data around human population, health, and income while shattering long held beliefs about their connections. Simon Sinek (see Resources again) made us rethink how to inspire action by focusing on the "why." Nobel peace prize nominated sixteen-year-old Greta Thunberg (see Resources yet again) offers a powerful voice for climate change action, succeeding where many before her have failed.

TED talks follow a simple yet highly effective structure. With an eighteen-minute maximum, they pack a lot into a relatively short time. This means speakers must be succinct and distill big ideas into a tight delivery. Many presenters work with coaches to craft and deliver maximum impact, and so can you. These talks are also a very instructive model for scientists hoping to engage wide ranges of audiences. After reviewing dozens of TED talks and speaking with a few of their presenters, we have documented a few key lessons you can use for your next speaking opportunity.

CREATE A STORY THAT COMMUNICATES WHY AUDIENCES SHOULD CARE

Scientists are used to the introduction, methods, research, analysis, and discussion (IMRaD) format, so it can be difficult for them to think about how to present information outside of that construct. That formula works well for scientific publications and presentations. However, science communication needs to reach out and grab a more general audience.

Let's consider a different approach. If you aren't speaking to a scientific group, develop a story arc that engages audiences at the very beginning, starting with an attention-grabbing fact, then moves along to include compelling information that makes your case and leaves your audience with a satisfying summary. Avoid jargon to keep things broadly understandable. Along the way, don't forget to tell people why you were interested in this work to begin with. Personal stories engage people much more than pure numbers. Statistics don't create an emotional bond with your audience. Instead, try pulling out a specific example or two that highlight the problem.

When thinking about the flow of your presentation, don't neglect to identify your overall objective—your big idea. Whatever it is you want people to know or do after your presentation, ensure you are effectively communicating that to them. Sounds obvious, we know, but you might be surprised at how often that isn't done and the big idea gets buried.

We tend to think of the range of options for objectives as falling between increased awareness (education), dialogue and feedback (engagement), and action (effecting change). Just like TED talks help people understand *how* what you are talking about is relevant to them. Just because you think they should care about it is not enough. Put yourself in their shoes and try to understand the issue from their perspective. If you haven't already viewed Simon Sinek's TED talk, it's worth a look. In it, he breaks down why defining and sharing your own "why" is so important.

If your audience doesn't "feel" your message, they won't be moved by it.

BE PRESENT AND CONNECT

Be present and strive to have a conversation with your audience. TED talk presenters are usually well-rehearsed before going on stage. Public speaking doesn't come easy to most people. It may take a lot of practice to look and feel natural on stage. Many people literally fear public speaking more than death (Croston, 2012). That's some deep-rooted fear! To quote Jerry Seinfeld:

> "This means to the average person, if you go to a funeral, you're better off in the casket than giving the eulogy."

To compensate for the anxiety of having to present in public, some speakers hide behind the podium and their PowerPoint slides, so they are completely disconnected with their audience. Remember, people came to hear your ideas. They want you to share your expertise and excitement with them. Consider stepping away from the podium. Make eye contact while you're speaking, and don't read off the slides. Slides should be a backdrop and guide for your presentation, not a literal translation of it. It's also helpful to assess the body language and facial expressions of your audience members. Take cues from their responses. Ask questions of the audience and answer later in the presentation. Do they seem to be following what you're saying? Do they seem to agree or disagree? Do they look confused? If your format allows, leave time for questions, and create conversations around your topic. That will provide a much richer experience for you and your audience.

WHEN YOUR AUDIENCE JUST WANTS TO DISRUPT: DIRTY DISINFORMATION DEEDS

Which brings us to the part of developing your narrative when someone is going to try and throw you off track and attempt to combat fact with disinformation or take the conversation way into the weeds. The central tenet of this approach is if you don't like the conversation, change it. The anti-fact crowd has done that, and environmental communicators have not responded fast or effectively enough.

Paula spoke with Dr. Carl Hershner, professor and frequent public speaker from the College of William and Mary's, Virginia Institute of Marine Science about his experience combatting disinformation. Hershner's work has included decades of research on wetlands and climate change, and he's often asked to present on these topics. He said that around 2010, he began noticing a trend of certain members of the public purposely trying to derail discussions with completely made-up conspiracy stories. They weren't asking him questions about data or implying that his work was wrong. In fact, they didn't really want to talk about his work at all. They wanted to talk about conspiracy theories; in the specific case he referenced, audiences kept mentioning a secret global plan to steal private property. It was complete fiction and not worth repeating in detail here. Maybe they truly believed it or perhaps they just wanted to divert attention from having other people talk about the looming climate crisis.

Regardless of their motivation, Paula asked Hershner if he had found effective ways of responding to them. "You just can't communicate with them because they're not there to do that; they don't care. They were there for confrontation, and avoiding that confrontation confused them."

Hershner said that one of the most valuable lessons he learned over the course of his long career is the importance of persistence. "I can't tell you the number of times when frustration with unsuccessful communication engenders an 'I give up' feeling. Succumbing to that means ignorance or misunderstanding wins, and you ultimately fail. While it can take years, and multiple tries, sometimes the effort finally pays off. Then the challenge is to internalize the joy of that moment so it can carry you through all the other setbacks."

In essence, don't lose hope or sight of your overall goal and the importance of your message. Scientists are used to being challenged by colleagues who play by the same rules they do. We know first-hand it can be very unsettling to combat misinformation or disinformation by someone who does not play by any of those rules. Disrupters are not typically supported by peer reviews or credible research, and they suffer no consequences for their actions. They appeal to the human inclination toward confirmation bias, and if you are delivering a message that may be difficult for people to accept, say around climate change and sea level rise, you must be steadfastly prepared for the long game.

Disrupters want to disrupt, whether in person, online, or in the press. You cannot control their behaviors, but you can prepare for them and respond appropriately. Responding without hostility is important because doing so only creates more of an "us versus them" situation. Intellectuals are often dismissed by being labeled as elite or arrogant, so don't play into that narrative and sabotage your goals by responding with anger. Wherever possible, look for learning opportunities to create shared understanding and accept that 100 percent agreement may not be realistic.

It is important to note that not everyone who disagrees is there to disrupt or spread falsehoods. There are often very legitimate grounds for disagreement, if not around the science itself, over what to do with that science.

Given all of that, here are several dos and don'ts for dealing with skeptical (and remember, some skepticism is healthy) audiences:

1. Do listen to your audiences. Everyone wants to be heard, and listening will provide you insight into their motivations and values.
2. Do remain calm and focused. Don't take the bait to be distracted and go off course.
3. Do bring the discussion back to the facts, based on trusted research.
4. Do seek to find common ground and shared learning, wherever that is possible.
5. Don't repeat disinformation lines or phrases. Doing that puts you in the position of providing more airtime for the wrong messages.
6. Don't react with contempt or anger. While that may provide a fleeting moment of satisfaction, it won't do anything to win over new audiences and convince disrupters they are wrong.
7. Don't give up. Celebrate your communication wins, large and small, to remain hopeful.

CHAPTER FIVE TAKE HOME TIPS

1. Don't just tell facts, share stories. Remember the old adage: Show, don't tell. Use data to develop compelling and engaging narratives to illustrate your main points. Try using specific data points to highlight what you're seeing or weave a narrative around the "so what" of your work.
2. Use equivalencies to put numbers into some context for your audiences.
3. Make sure you let your audience know why they should care. How does it impact them? What does it mean for them?

4. At some point, you are very likely to face opposition and possibly even hostility to your work. As they say, the best time to prepare for a crisis is when you are not in crisis. So, prepare for a disruptive situation by considering how you would apply the suggestions provided in the section above.

RESOURCES

1. For insight on overcoming misinformation, read *A Survival Guide to the Misinformation Age: Scientific Habits of Mind,* by David J. Helfand.
2. Subscribe to *The Story Collider* podcast to hear science stories told on stage.
3. Because you can never have too many podcast recommendations, also subscribe to Alie Ward's *Ologies*, a comedic science show and named one of *Time Magazine*'s top fifty podcasts.
4. To see a true data-based storytelling master in his element, check out the Hans Rosling TED Talk gallery, "The Best Hans Rosling Talks You've Ever Seen," at *https://www.TED.com/Playlists/474/The_Best_Hans_Rosling_Talks_Yo.*
5. Learn how to share your "why" by reading Simon Sinek's book, *Start with Why: How Great Leaders Inspire Action.*
6. Want to be inspired? Check out Greta Thunberg's TED talk, "The Disarming Case to Act Right Now on Climate Change," at *https://www.TED.com/Talks/Greta_Thunberg_The_Disarming_Case_To_Act_Right_Now_On_Climate_Change.*
7. You should have a copy of Nancy Duarte's *Data Story: Explain Data and Inspire Action Through Story* by your desk at all times.

CHAPTER SIX

VISUALIZATION

"By visualizing information, we turn it into a landscape that you can explore with your eyes: a sort of information map. And when you're lost in information, an information map is kind of useful."

—DAVID MCCANDLESS

To really amp up communication and connecting with your audiences, it's critical to bring visual elements into your outreach efforts. In the grand scheme of things, we've been visual communicators for as long as we've been humans. Cave paintings dating back more than thirty thousand years have been found in France and Indonesia. These images depict human forms interspersed with drawings of animals, likely depicting stories of the hunt. Even as we moved beyond cave paintings and established complex writing systems, visual elements are an important part of communicating and teaching. Numerous studies have shown that "effective use of visuals can decrease learning time, improve comprehension, enhance retrieval, and increase retention" (Kouyoumdijan, 2012).

These visual elements can include graphs, maps, diagrams, infographics, and videos. These can be combined into final communications products including fact sheets, web pages, reports, and interpretive signage. There is a broad spectrum of development skill involved both across and within each of these elements. In other words, someone who can make graphs in Excel may have no idea about how to create a map (or even the software required). And, while one individual might be able to gin up a basic graphic in Excel, another might be able to take that graph into a graphic design software and turn it into something worthy of publication in the science section of the *New York Times.*

Regardless of where you fall on the skill spectrum, understanding some basic guidelines to communicating visually will help ensure whatever visual elements you include with your communication efforts are telling your story as effectively as possible. Even if you decide to let someone else do the design heavy lifting, you will at least know what to look for and have an informed understanding of the process. What we are providing here are some general tips on things to think about when developing visual communications products. This will not be a how-to guide. There are too many different software packages and techniques for us to provide a definitive guide to developing specific communications products. We will discuss a few kinds of visual elements, such as charts and infographics, and then review communications products, like fact sheets and interpretive signage, where these elements are brought together based on what has worked for us personally as well as when teachings others.

CHARTS

Let's start with the most basic of visual communication elements: graphs and charts. As anyone who has worked with spreadsheet applications for any length of time knows, there are many different flavors of graphs and charts. While it may be relatively easy to enter your data and generate a chart, there are some important things to consider to ensure your chart is communicating clearly. Although spreadsheet graphing has gotten better over the years, the default results that applications spit out can definitely be improved upon. We'll step you through a few things to consider and provide tips for making charts and graphs easier for your audience to understand.

The first question you might ask is, "What's the difference between a graph and a chart?" Charts display data that has been analyzed or categorized. Common examples are pie charts or bar charts. Graphs are a type of chart that is used to show raw data or mathematical relationships between data, such as trends or correlations. The most common example of a graph is a scatter plot. The bottom line is that all graphs are charts but not all charts are graphs.

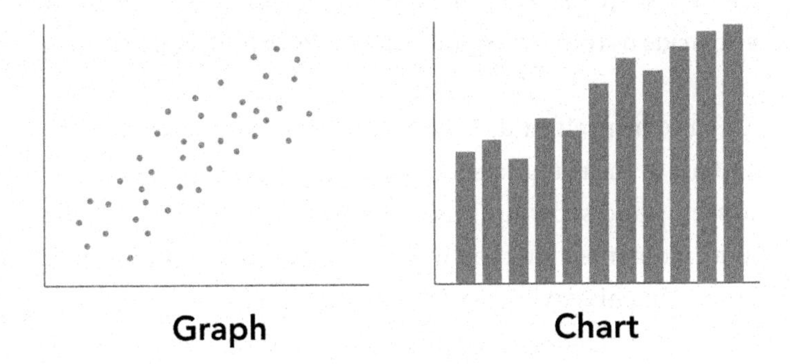

What makes a chart good? There are several different factors to consider when designing your chart, and we will discuss some of them. However, we feel the most important guiding principle should be efficient design. It may be an overused term, but when it comes to chart design (and the design of any other information graphic), less really is more. Efficient design means the chart is uncluttered so that the data can clearly and effectively tell its story.

One of the leading figures in good chart design is Edward Tufte, a pioneer in the field of data visualization. Tufte was a professor of political science, public affairs, statistics, and computer science at Princeton and Yale. He was enlisted by the Obama administration to help advise on how the data about where and on what the stimulus funds were spent were displayed on the Recovery.gov website. Years ago, well before we launched Green Fin Studio, we had the good fortune to participate in one of his daylong workshops that drew participants from multiple disciplines, from medical, military, and environmentalists, like us. Like his several available books, his workshop provided techniques on how to make charts clear and understandable as well as real world examples of charts that are confusing and either purposely or accidentally misleading. Tufte helped us not only see data in new ways, but it also made us think differently about how to present it to others.

As Tufte himself said, "The commonality between science and art is in trying to see profoundly to develop strategies of seeing and showing." His workshop was one of our many "aha" moments along the way. We knew data was powerful, but leaving his daylong workshop was akin to emerging from a data visualization chrysalis—if there were such a thing.

While Tufte might have a lot to say about the design of charts and graphs, perhaps one of his most important pieces of advice is there should be no wasted ink. What this means is that any pixel on a chart should be there to convey information. If it isn't helping to tell the data's story, then it is only cluttering up the chart. Tufte refers to this as "chart junk" (Tufte, 1997).

Based on Tufte's advice and some insight from our own experience, we offer the following list of chart junk to avoid:

- **Images or patterns used to fill the background of a chart or chart element.** Just because you can add a picture of a forest to the background of your chart about tree growth doesn't mean you should. Background images generally only make the data hard to see and do little to help tell the story of the data.
- **Vertical or horizontal grid lines that dominate the chart.** While gridlines may help the viewer orient data points in the middle of a chart, they are generally not very helpful for most charts used when communicating with the general public. The viewer should be able to see the general patterns in the data without the aid of gridlines. If this isn't possible, then you should ask yourself if the data you are showing is really telling a story. If you feel you must use gridlines, you should make them a subtle as possible (think thin and light gray).
- **Unnecessary chart legends.** If you are creating a chart of monthly precipitation in Richmond, Virginia, and your chart title clearly states this, then there is no need to have a legend on your chart indicating that each point displayed represent monthly precipitation.

In the image below we compare two charts of the same atmospheric CO_2 levels. The "bad" chart shows an egregious overuse of some of the chart junk available in spreadsheet applications, while the "good" chart is an example of a clean and effective format. Let's list off the offenses of the bad chart:

1. **A meaningless 3D effect applied to the bars**. Adding another dimension does not convey any information from the data.
2. **Each bar uniquely colored.** There are no differences among the points that necessitates coloring them differently, and doing so suggests that there is. The only difference is the year, and that is already covered by the X axis labels.
3. **Horizontal grid lines.** With the data that is plotted, the gridlines don't really add much in the way of conveying information given that the differences between years and over the entire time span is obvious. If the data points were closer together in value or there was a less obvious trend over time, gridlines might be useful for data interpretation. Otherwise, leave them out.
4. **Glow and drop shadow effects.** As used here, they convey no additional information about the data. Used more judiciously, such as to call attention to a single data point, the glow effect might be effective.
5. **Background image**. That's Cooper, the family cat, and although he's freaking awesome, he has no business appearing in the background of a chart. Neither do any other types of images. Don't do it… ever. We mean it!

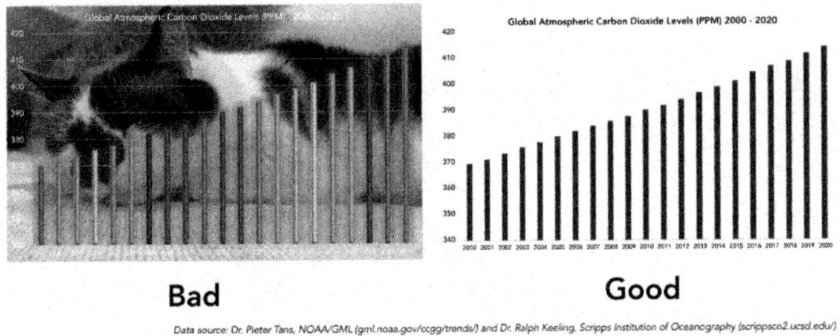

Keep in mind there is a difference between meaningless design features that add nothing to or even distract from the data story and adding supplemental and supportive information to a chart. If there is a particular data point that you want to call attention to that is important to your narrative, call it out right there on the chart. Don't feel you have to restrict your commentary to the chart caption.

As an example, in 2017 we released a text about the Chesapeake Bay (Jasinski et al., 2017). It features a chapter on the impacts of climate change on the Bay. Since the text is meant for a general audience, we did not want to assume the average reader understood the difference between weather and climate. Therefore, we developed a graphic that compared the long-term average temperatures between Minneapolis, Minnesota, and Miami, Florida. These long-term temperatures are indicative of the climate in each of these cities. The graphs also included the average daily temperature for each day in 2015 for each city. These daily temperatures are the weather. The point of the graph is that weather can be highly variable while climate is consistent. It even shows that Minneapolis and Miami can occasionally have very similar weather in terms of temperature.

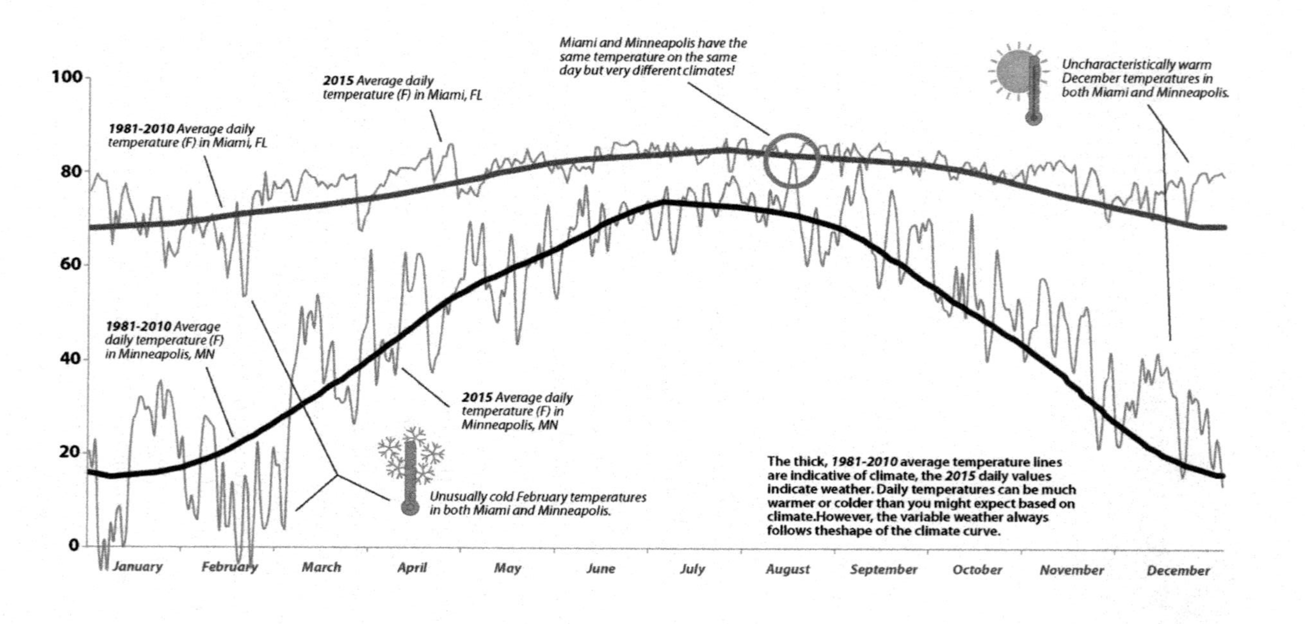
Miami and Minneapolis have the same temperature on the same day but very different climates!
2015 Average daily temperature (F) in Miami, FL
Uncharacteristically warm December temperatures in both Miami and Minneapolis.
1981-2010 Average daily temperature (F) in Miami, FL
100
80
60
40
20
0
1981-2010 Average daily temperature (F) in Minneapolis, MN
2015 Average daily temperature (F) in Minneapolis, MN
Unusually cold February temperatures in both Miami and Minneapolis.
The thick, 1981-2010 average temperature lines are indicative of climate, the 2015 daily values indicate weather. Daily temperatures can be much warmer or colder than you might expect based on climate.However, the variable weather always follows theshape of the climate curve.
January
February
March
April
May
June
July
August
September
October
November
December

To help tell this story, we used descriptive text right in the graphic with lines to call out specific data points. We even circled a day in mid-August when both cities had the same average temperature that day. By telling the story right on the chart, it helps to make the information more understandable to a wider audience.

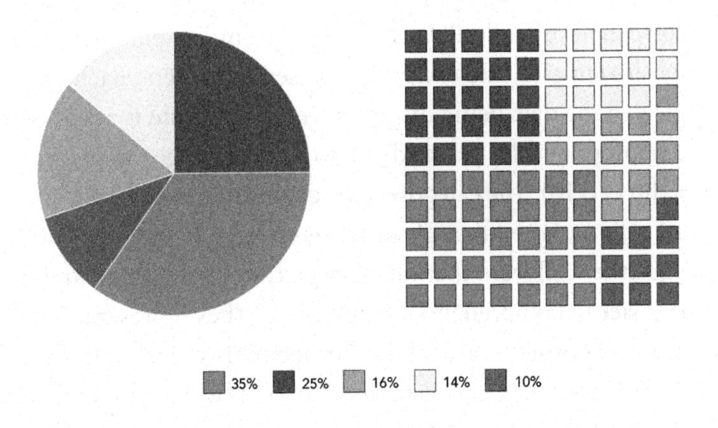

One of the go-to chart types for showing the percent make-up of different categories within a data set is the pie chart. In recent years, it is also one of the more disparaged chart types. One of the main arguments against them is that people are not terribly good at distinguishing differences in each slice of pie in a pie chart. Obviously, when comparing a slice that represents 65 percent of the date to one that represents 15 percent, people will not have trouble identifying the larger slice. But what about identifying the larger of a 16 percent and 14 percent slice (as in the image above)? Another issue is that small percentage slices (<2 percent) can be difficult to even see on most normal sized charts. A possible solution is to label each of the slices with the percentage value, though this can make a chart look cluttered. It might just be easier to display the values in a table.

Truth be told, we have used pie charts, but only when there are relatively few categories or slices and the differences in the percentages are large enough to easily distinguish between the different slices. An alternative to the pie chart that we're fond of is the waffle chart (Hey, if you can't have pie, at least you can have waffles!). In its simplest form, a waffle chart is a ten-by-ten grid, and each cell represents 1 percent. Each category in the data being displayed gets a color and is assigned a number of cells that adds up to its percentage (30 percent = thirty cells). The categories are distributed in the grid, and all cells assigned to a given category have to touch at least one other cell from that category, so they are clustered and it is easier to comprehend the percentage they represent. This method doesn't really allow for decimals unless you want to increase the grid size to one hundred by one hundred so that each ten cells represent 1 percent. On the waffle chart, discerning the difference between these categories is facilitated by the fact that the viewer can simply count the squares to know one is different than the other and by how much.

In the image above, we've plotted the same data using a pie chart and a waffle chart. In the pie chart, seeing the percent differences between the categories is easy when the differences are fairly large. However, seeing the difference between the 14 percent and 16 percent is a bit more difficult.

If you are feeling creative, instead of grid cells use icons that are representative of each category of data. Just be sure that the icons have the same design scheme (i.e. look like they belong together) and are shown in the same size on the chart.

MAPS

In our decades of communicating about environmental science, we've had the amazingly good fortune to work on hundreds of projects with a broad spectrum of clients, many of them needing to communicate with stakeholders about a specific idea or turn data into information. While each of these projects have had their own unique goals, there is one thing that more than 95 percent of them have had in common: maps. Whether they were the central focus of the project or simply used to provide context, we consistently rely on the power of maps to convey information efficiently and effectively.

In many cases, it is the client who is leading the charge with wanting a map. They understand that maps are powerful communication tools and already know they will help to tell their story. So if the power of maps is nothing new, then why even bring it up, right? As with charts, there are some strategies that will help make your maps more effective.

The primary piece of advice when it comes to maps is that simpler is better. Apart from the data or location that you want to inform people about, you should show a base map with geographic features and landmarks that give people a frame of reference. Anything else should be left off the map. Hill shades might look nice, but unless they add to the message it's a detail that isn't needed. Roads are a nice way for people to orient themselves and can give them a good frame of reference for the area or areas you are highlighting. However, only show roads that are relevant to the scale of your map. Major interstates are great for state or multistate maps, but streets and boulevards may not even be visible, or if they are, will only make the map look cluttered. In the maps below we show the difference between a map with a lot of unnecessary details and one that spares the details so the viewer can get a better sense of what is being presented.

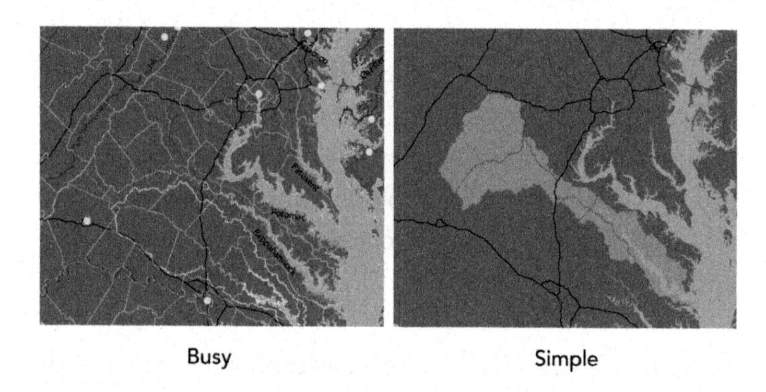

Busy Simple

If you are developing a map of a relatively small region such as a county, it is helpful to provide viewers with some spatial context for the location of that county within its state. Inset maps are an effective way of doing this. These are small maps placed in a corner of the main map that have a much broader geographic scope. In the example of the county map, the inset map would show an outline of the state with the county highlighted within it. Inset maps should be kept very simple as their only point is to provide spatial context for the larger map.

Keep your maps simple to allow your data to take center stage.

INFOGRAPHICS

Infographics have become increasingly popular in recent years. These combine charts, maps, diagrams, and text to tell visual stories about a subject. They say that a picture is worth a thousand words, and because they have so many graphical elements, a well-designed infographic may be worth ten thousand words or more. One of the nice things about infographics is that there aren't really any rules to developing them and the designs can range from simple to complex.

A simply designed infographic might consist of some points of information and then basic icons that illustrate the information contained in each point. The point of the graphics is just to make the information more engaging. For example, maybe you want to create an infographic for the steps of planting a tree. Each step would consist of one or two sentences and icons of a shovel, a hole in the ground, a tree, and a hose would be placed next to the text for each step. The icons may not provide much in the way of information, but they do make the information more engaging, which may make people more apt to read it.

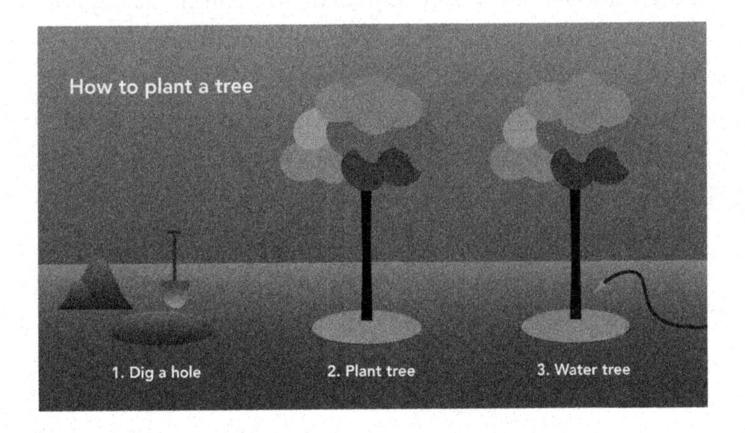

Moving toward more complex infographics, the visuals do most of the talking. We were asked to develop an infographic that described the sources and impact of nutrient pollution to the Chesapeake Bay. The client was interested in comparing the magnitude of the different sources, and we thought that a visualization would aide in in discussions about regulating this pollution.

Searching for inspiration, we went to David MaCandless's website, InformationIsBeautiful.net. This site is a must-see for people interested in infographics and the many ways to design and execute them. While browsing through the website, we found an infographic that illustrated some facts about the greenhouse gas methane and its sources. It provided some background information about what methane is and then graphically compared the magnitude of its various sources. We realized that with some adjustments, we could use the same type of design for our nutrient pollution graphic.

The infographic provides the viewer with some background information on nutrient pollution relative to Chesapeake Bay. It then describes the major sources of nutrients in the Bay and the magnitude of each. The infographic finishes with details on the impacts nutrient pollution has on the health of the Chesapeake ecosystem. Icons are used throughout to illustrate the various points discussed, and many of the graphical elements are driven by actual data. We kept the color pallet simple so that attention is paid to the information being conveyed, not to excess colors that don't signify anything.

A watershed scale look at nutrients and the Chesapeake Bay

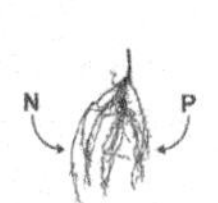

Nitrogen (N) and Phosphorus (P) are important plant nutrients found in both fertilizer and occuring naturally in the environment. When they enter the Bay in excess quantities, they are disruptive to the ecosystem.

The amount of N and P that enters the Bay each year (load) is directly related to river flow.
More Precipitation = More Nutrients

Nutrients fuel the Bay's extremely produtive food chain. However, an overload of nutrients is detrimental and the Bay has been suffering from this overload for several decades.

While progress has been made managing nutrient inputs, the climate has been changing, population has been increasing, and development has been expanding. These stressors can increase nutrient inputs and make progress difficult.

Where do nutrients come from?*

In 2017, total estimated inputs of nutrients into Chesapeake Bay were:

253 million pounds N **15** million pounds P

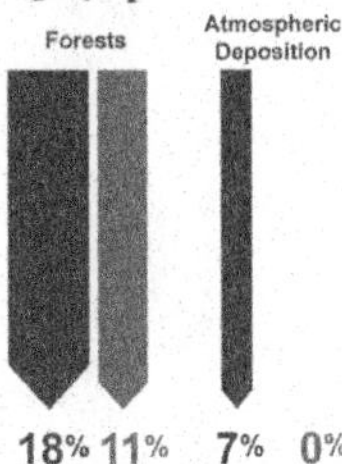
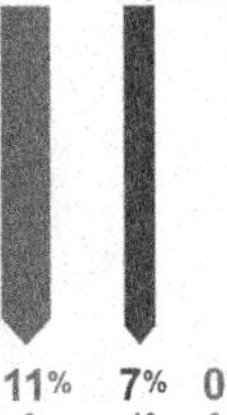

	Agriculture		Urban Stormwater Runoff		Wastewater		Septic		Forests		Atmospheric Deposition	
	N	P	N	P	N	P	N	P	N	P	N	P
%	42%	56%	16%	18%	13%	15%	4%	0%	18%	11%	7%	0%
million pounds	106	8	41	3	33	2	9	0	46	2	16	0

Water Clarity

Excess nutrients washing into the Bay fuel an overabundance or bloom of algae living there. Too much algae causes a cascade of problems starting with a loss of water clarity.

A decrease in water clarity means that sunlight can not penetrate into the water making it difficult for underwater plants (submerged aquatic vegetation or SAV) to grow.

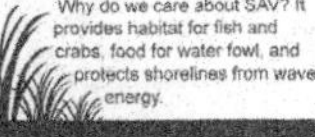

Why do we care about SAV? It provides habitat for fish and crabs, food for water fowl, and protects shorelines from wave energy.

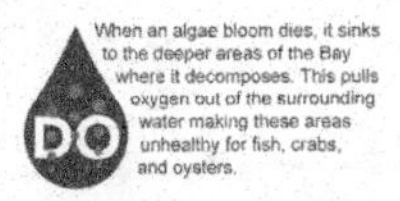

When an algae bloom dies, it sinks to the deeper areas of the Bay where it decomposes. This pulls oxygen out of the surrounding water making these areas unhealthy for fish, crabs, and oysters.

Excess nutrients can also fuel the growth of harmful algae which give off toxins that can harm fish, shellfish, turtles, marine mammals and humans.

*Nutrient load data are for the entire Chesapeake Bay.
Nutrient load and flow data from USGS (https://www.chesapeakeprogress.com/clean-water/water-quality)
Nutrient input data is model generated 2017 data from the Chesapeake Bay Program (https://www.chesapeakeprogress.com/clean-water/watershed-implementation-plans)

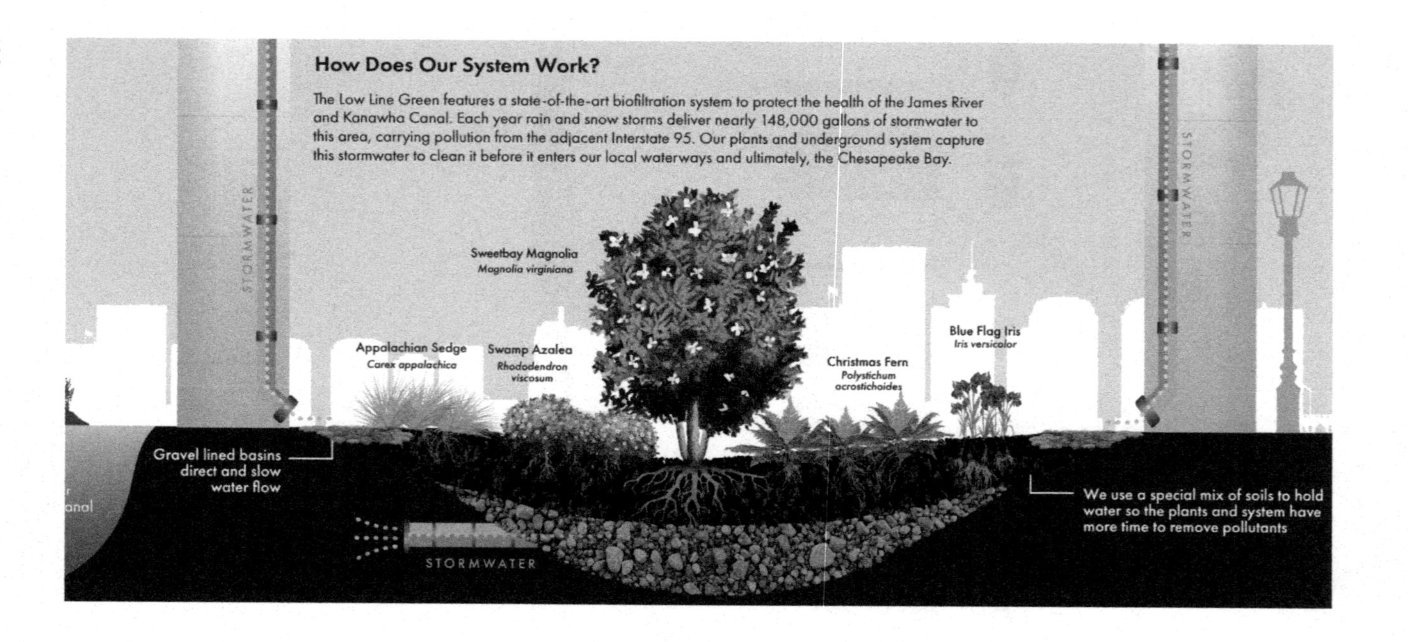
How Does Our System Work?
The Low Line Green features a state-of-the-art biofiltration system to protect the health of the James River and Kanawha Canal. Each year rain and snow storms deliver nearly 148,000 gallons of stormwater to this area, carrying pollution from the adjacent Interstate 95. Our plants and underground system capture this stormwater to clean it before it enters our local waterways and ultimately, the Chesapeake Bay.
STORMWATER
STORMWATER
Sweetbay Magnolia
Magnolia virginiana
Appalachian Sedge
Carex appalachica
Swamp Azalea
Rhododendron viscosum
Christmas Fern
Polystichum acrostichoides
Blue Flag Iris
Iris versicolor
Gravel lined basins direct and slow water flow
STORMWATER
We use a special mix of soils to hold water so the plants and system have more time to remove pollutants

Another type of infographic we often use is the conceptual diagram. This is a visualization of a process or concept. It is essentially a picture with labels and minimal explanatory text. Many infographics tend to be linear in that information tends to be given in order, top to bottom or left to right. For the most part, conceptual diagrams present all the information in one block, allowing the user to take in the information in any order they wish. There is generally a spatial aspect to this type of infographic. It represents an actual or example physical space, and the location of various details in the graphic are directly related to locations in a real-world environment.

We find conceptual diagrams to be particularly useful in interpretive signage where the sign is placed in front of an environmental feature such as a rain garden. Using a conceptual diagram of the garden in front of the sign, features and functions of the garden can be identified and simply explained.

WHAT NOW?

This has been a very cursory review of some options you might consider for visually communicating. We hope you will take our advice to heart when developing your own visual elements. The road to communications hell is paved with well-intended but poorly designed graphics. Once you have developed the graphics, the obvious question is what to do next. Options for distributing your communications materials with these graphics incorporated are numerous. We outline a few here.

FACT SHEETS

Fact sheets are a great way to distill a lot of information into a small space. Typically the front and back of a single page, well-designed fact sheets feature engaging visuals, and text is limited to short paragraphs and bullet points. They will allow someone to briefly skim through and be able to get a sense of what your message is, why they should care, and what they can do. You can also use them for talking points when speaking with someone one-on-one. Invest the time to make sure the text is concise and informative.

WEBSITES

All websites benefit from engaging visuals, and there is no better place to display your freshly minted charts, maps, and infographics than your webpage. When designing visuals for use on the web, it is important to think about how they will display on different screen sizes. Remember, many people will be visiting your website on their mobile device.

SOCIAL MEDIA

Simple graphs are great for use on social media. To make the best use of the real estate these platforms provide, format visuals to be square, if possible. Infographics, which tend to be larger in size with a lot of details, often don't display well on these platforms. Since many infographics are divided into sections of information, you can create standalone social media graphics from these sections.

CHAPTER SIX TAKE HOME TIPS

1. In all your visualization efforts, always remember that simpler is better. Clutter on a chart or graphic is like clutter on a messy desk—it makes it hard to concentrate and find what you are looking for.
2. Even if you are not the one developing the graphics, apply what you've learned here to offer edits and make what is produced better.
3. Next time you need to communicate a complex process or system, consider using an infographic.

RESOURCES

1. Read Nancy Duarte's book, *Resonate: Present Visual Stories That Transform Audiences.* Her work never fails to give us new ideas.
2. Check out any of Edward Tufte's books, including *The Visual Display of Quantitative Information*, *Envisioning Information*, and *Visual Explanations.*
3. Spend some time wandering around David McCandless's website and check out how he does infographics. Maybe sign up for a course while you're there at InformationIsBeautiful.net.

CHAPTER SEVEN

FINAL THOUGHTS

We opened our environmental communications company, Green Fin Studio, more than a decade ago. Over that time, the goals have remained largely the same: broaden the base of support around environmental issues; bring diverse stakeholders together to collaboratively develop solutions to complex problems; and find ways to communicate complex information so that it is understandable, interesting, and relatable to groups with diverse backgrounds and interests.

Over this time, our understanding of how to reach these goals has evolved. With that evolution has come an improvement in our ability to meaningfully connect with audiences and affect change. As we conclude, we would like to bring it home with what we feel are some of the more important recommendations made in this book.

UNDERSTAND PEOPLE'S MOTIVATIONS

Ever been stuck in a conversation at a party with someone who is a big fan of a particular topic such as sports or a TV show or a book that you have either never heard of or have no interest in? When you are in this kind of interaction it can often feel like you are being talked at instead of being part of a conversation. It isn't terribly enjoyable, it's hard to pay attention, and you just want it to be over.

The point of this is to say that an important part of environmental communications is to understand that just because you are passionate about a particular subject or cause does not mean other people will be. You need to understand this before you even begin your communications efforts. Otherwise, there will be only efforts and no results. And as we have made the point repeatedly in this book, blasting everyone with a bunch of facts and figures about your subject or cause is not going to win you any converts. Remember, the information deficit model is not correct.

However, that doesn't mean you can't get people to support and contribute to your cause using the methods we've outlined in this book. You just need to help them realize that helping you fix the issues you have identified benefits them. This may upset some purists who feel that people should do the right thing because it's the right thing. To them we say, Get over it! The reality is that we're dealing with humans, and while most of us have a decent moral compass, we're kind of wired to look out for our own self interests. That doesn't necessarily make us bad, it just makes us human. In the end, not everyone needs to have the same reasons for supporting your mission.

INCLUDE COMMUNICATION FROM THE BEGINNING

We have honestly lost track of the number of times a research or environmental restoration group has come to us with a desperate need to communicate about their program or results but with no funds set aside to cover the costs. As we said in chapter one, the best time to discuss and plan for communication products is at the beginning, including while you are writing the project proposal. This will ensure you have thought through what communications should happen around your project and that funds exist to support the communication process. Having a plan for communication will be attractive to funders, will help ensure that information about your program and results are widely disseminated, and possibly be a factor in securing future funding.

Time, effort, and money invested in good design will pay dividends. From presentations to fliers to posters to website to social media, well-executed design will capture and hold people's attention. For passive communication products like printed materials and websites, attention paid to how things are laid out helps ensure they are easy to read and that the reader can understand the relationship of the items on the page. It's a hard enough battle to get people to engage with your science or cause; don't put up hurdles in the form of bad design to make things more difficult.

Well-designed communication products make the job of presenting them easier because it means you can spend less time explaining them and more time engaging your audience with your story. It's like delivering a joke: If you have to explain it, it either wasn't very funny in the first place or you did a bad job telling it. And for all types of communication products, good design speaks to your audiences in another way. If you haven't cared enough to take the time and effort to make engaging and understandable communications, then why should your audiences take the time and effort to read them?

KNOW AND UNDERSTAND YOUR AUDIENCES

Take the initiative and energy to truly understand your audiences and their motivations and work to connect with them on their terms. As discussed in chapter two, don't assume you understand your audience's feelings about a topic or issue. For example, environmental organizations and agencies are often involved in efforts to get stakeholders to adopt new behavior or policies. People generally don't like change, and they often have preconceived notions about the impacts of change. If you have the time and capacity, set up phone interviews with individuals from your target audience or audiences. Ask them questions to determine their interest and knowledge of the issue, their concerns, and what questions they have. Knowing this information is better than assuming you know and allows you to develop messaging that addresses concerns and questions directly.

Once you have a better understanding of your audience, you might try developing a few user personas as described in chapter four to further characterize and understand them. We have developed personas to help several of our clients better understand their audiences. Nine times out of ten they start the exercise by rolling their eyes thinking the idea is silly and then finish with a smile and better understanding of their stakeholders.

KEEP YOUR LANGUAGE SIMPLE BUT SMART

When speaking with folks who are "outside the tent," make the effort to communicate in terms that are understandable to broader audiences. Do not look at this through a lens of "dumbing things down"; instead, think of this as making things clearer and easier to understand. As we discussed in chapter four, jargon is so toxic that even if you define the jargon you use, it still impacts people's perception of the material presented. Besides, jargon is a crutch, and developing your messages without it will help you to become a better communicator.

As discussed in chapter five, when you need to talk about big numbers, use equivalencies to put things in human terms. Numbers with a lot of commas and zeros may look impressive but can be difficult for people to conceptualize and, like jargon, may leave them scratching their heads. So, using an equivalency you might say something like, "Our study area was sixty-four thousand acres or one hundred square miles or about five times the area of Manhattan."

FOCUS ON POSITIVE SOLUTIONS

These days, if you are in an environmental field and are attempting to communicate with stakeholders, it is more than likely you're trying to avert an ecological catastrophe. Unfortunately, that is the reality of where we are right now. Remember, as we discussed in chapter three, hope is a better motivator than doom. So, remember to focus on what is possible and what we can accomplish, not just on how bad things are. It is a tough balancing act because it is difficult to communicate a hopeful outlook while letting people know the severity of the situation you are trying to enlist their help in solving. For far too long, climate change communications focused primarily on the grim reality of an increasingly warming planet without framing possible solutions. Always consider what you want your audiences to do with the information beyond merely increasing their awareness.

To help keep the message positive and in tune with your audiences, it may be helpful to think about how you are framing your messages. Take another look at the second table in chapter three for some ideas about this.

TELL A STORY

You must include storytelling in your communications toolbox. As we said in chapter four, humans are wired for it. The next time you are putting together a presentation about your research, think about structuring it like a story. Introduce yourself (or someone else) as the hero, the problem you wanted to solve or understand and your efforts to do so, and finish with your victorious result. If you are communicating with a group of stakeholders whose behavior you want to change, try telling a success story of a stakeholder who took action and is thrilled with the results. Your audience will be more likely to remember your message and more likely to act based on it.

VISUALIZATIONS MAKE GREAT COMMUNICATIONS AWESOME

People have written entire books on charts alone, and we had a single chapter where we discussed charts, maps, and infographics. It was admittedly a whirlwind tour, but we hope it at least inspired you to dig deeper into what is possible with each of these options. As you explore different techniques and tools for creating your visuals, we hope you keep one piece of advice in mind: Keep it clean and simple. Consider each pixel you put on a chart. Does it add information or clutter? Does its color or position add to or distract from the story you are trying to tell? Keeping these simple things in mind can make the difference between a good graphic and a great graphic.

LOOK FOR INSPIRATION EVERYWHERE

Once you start thinking about the importance of clear and engaging messaging and visuals, you will start to notice the techniques of others: how they craft their messages, how they are inviting you to be a part of their effort, clever things they've done in how they've designed their visuals. Trust us, it won't just be communication products from other science and environmental groups. You'll see things in the way an insurance company communicates a campaign or how a food delivery app explains their service in a simple graphic that'll make you think, "I could use that approach in the fact sheet we have to develop this week." Apply these in your own work. Modify, adjust, and make it your own. Heck, in chapter three we even recommended using the techniques of the guy who helped politicize the climate issue, because while we do not support his objectives, we saw that they worked and can be used for "good."

Never stop learning and looking for ways to help others understand environmental issues. Scientific training provides a necessary foundation to understand our world, if not communicate that understanding to broad audiences. As we said at the beginning, there is now too much at stake for us to ignore the need to find new and better ways to connect with people around data, facts, and solutions. Science can lead the way if we, collectively, can provide and harness the power of effective marketing and communication strategies to win over hearts and minds.

ACKNOWLEDGMENTS

This book would not have been possible without the generous support, wisdom, and time of so many people. First and foremost, a huge and infinite thank you goes out to our family.

To our children, Sam and Eva, we do this, all of it, for you. Our most sincere wish is that we can play some small role in helping to make the world a better place for you and your children.

To our parents, thank you for your unwavering love and encouragement.

To the team at New Degree Press, especially Eric Koester, who supported us at every step of this book development. Our manuscript editors, Asa Loewenstein and Bianca DaSilva, were equal parts cheerleaders and copy editors. Thank you both for guiding us along different parts of this journey.

We were humbled and delighted by those who graciously submitted to interviews, including Randy Olson, PhD; Laura Lindendfeld, PhD; Walter Boynton, PhD; John Besley, PhD;

Carl Hershner, PhD; Katherine Rowan, PhD; and Amanda Stanley, PhD.

The list of dear friends, colleagues, mentors, and supporters who purchased an early copy helped us bring this book to life. Our most sincere and infinite thanks to James Anderson, Cheryl Andrews, Jill Baker, Nikki Bass, Marcia Berman, Jessica Blackburn, Walter Boynton, Elizabeth Chudoba, Meredeth Dash, Kristen Hughes Evans, Rachel Felver, Verna Harrison, Leesa Hernandez, Beth Hester, Roy Hoagland, Lisa Huffman, Karen Ingram, Stanley Jasinski, Shaheen Khan, Eric Koester, Cynthia Lewis, Jiangang Luo, Susan Mageau, Virginia Morris, David Parrish, Walter Priest, Rob Pritchard, Alex Rafii, Jessica Reid, Gina Sawaya, Emily Smedley, Elizabeth Smith, Rick and Ellie St. John, Meg Turner, and Michael Weyand. We also wish to thank those donors who wish to remain anonymous.

We cannot thank our beta readers enough: Rob Atkinson, PhD; Walter Boynton, PhD; Jonah Fogel; Robert Forloney; Samuel Lake, PhD; Siddhartha Mitra, PhD; Katherine Rowan, PhD; and Jackie Savitz. You all helped us sharpen our thoughts and make this book much stronger than it would have been otherwise.

Truly none of this would be possible without all the clients who have believed in us, worked with us throughout the years, and taught us something each and every day. We wish that we had room to list every single one of you here and thank you profusely. In addition to the people and organizations we have had the great good fortune of working with and for, we cannot overlook the fabulous staff we have on our team. We thank you all for joining us and supporting the dream to deliver creative and successful environmental communication strategies and products.

We have undoubtedly and accidentally forgotten someone, and for that, please forgive us. We could not have done this without the many teams and people supporting us.

APPENDIX

INTRODUCTION: WELCOME

Alan Alda Center for Communicating Science. "Home Page." Accessed October 1, 2021. *https://www.aldacenter.org.*

Chesapeake Bay Program. "Wetlands Work." Accessed October 1, 2021. *https://www.wetlandswork.org/.*

Masson-Delmotte, V., P. Zhai, A. Pirani, S.L. Connors, C. Péan, S. Berger, N. Caud, Y. Chen, L. Goldfarb, M.I. Gomis, M. Huang, K. Leitzell, E. Lonnoy, J.B.R. Matthews, T.K. Maycock, T.Waterfield, O. Yelekçi, R. Yu, and B. Zhou. *Climate Change 2021: The Physical Science Basis. Contribution of Working Group I to the Sixth Assessment Report of the Intergovernmental Panel on Climate Change.* IPPC: Cambridge University Press, 2021.

CHAPTER ONE: THE ART AND URGENCY OF ENVIRONMENTAL COMMUNICATION

Cash, David W., Jonathan C. Borck, and Anthony G. Patt. "Countering the Loading-Dock Approach to Linking Science and Decision Making: Comparative Analysis of El Niño/Southern Oscillation (ENSO) Forecasting Systems." *Science, Technol-*

ogy, & Human Values 31, no. 4 (July 2006): 465–94. *https://doi.org/10.1177/0162243906287547.*

Jasinski, David, Paula Jasinski, and Robert Wood. *Chesapeake Bay Ecosystem Atlas: An Interactive Guide to Chesapeake Bay.* Richmond, Virginia: Chesapeake Environmental Communications, 2017. *http://books.apple.com/us/book/id1020777102.*

Saint-Exupery, Antoine de. *The Little Prince.* Translated by Irene Testot-Ferry. Wordsworth Collector's Editions. Ware, England: Wordsworth Editions, 2018.

Science Counts. "Report Benchmark." Website PowerPoint, Accessed July 29, 2021. *https://www.sciencecounts.org/wp-content/uploads/2019/02/ReportBenchmark.pdf.*

Sinek, Simon. *Start with Why: How Great Leaders Inspire Everyone to Take Action.* New York: Portfolio, 2009.

CHAPTER TWO: LISTEN TO LEARN

Howell, Daniel, Amy M. Schueller, Jacob W. Bentley, Andre Buchheister, David Chagaris, Matthew Cieri, Katie Drew, Mathieu G. Lundy, Debbi Pedreschi, David G. Reid, and Howard Townsend. "Combining Ecosystem and Single-Species Modeling to Provide Ecosystem-Based Fisheries Management Advice Within Current Management Systems." *Front. Mar. Sci.,* January 8, 2021. doi: 10.3389/fmars.2020.607831.

Schwartz, John. "Katharine Hayhoe, a Climate Explainer Who Stays above the Storm." *The New York Times,* October 10, 2016. *https://www.nytimes.com/2016/10/11/science/katharine-hayhoe-climate-change-science.html.*

CHAPTER THREE: CONNECTING YOUR AUDIENCE AND MESSAGES

Brene Brown. "Brene Brown on Blame." February 4, 2015. Video, 3:25. *https://www.youtube.com/watch?v=RZWf2_2L2v8.*

Carnegie, Dale. *How to Win Friends and Influence People*. New York: Simon and Schuster, 1964.

Goldberg, Briar. "Before Your Next Presentation or Speech, Here's the First Thing You Must Think About." October 29, 2019. *https://ideas.ted.com/before-your-next-presentation-or-speech-heres-the-first-thing-you-must-think-about.*

Leiserowitz, A. "Communicating the Risks of Global Warming: American Risk Perceptions, Affective Images and Interpretive Communities." In *Creating a Climate for Change: Communicating Climate Change and Facilitating Social Change,* edited by S. Moser and L. Dilling, 44-63. Cambridge: Cambridge University Press, 2007.

Lorenzoni, I., Leiserowitz, A., De Franca Doria, M., Poortinga, W., and Pidgeon, N. 2006, April. Cross-national comparisons of image associations with "global warming" and "climate change" among laypeople in the United States of America and Great Britain. *Journal of Risk Research*, 9(3), 265-281.

Luntz, Frank. *Words That Work: It's Not What You Say, It's What People Hear.* New York, NY: Hyperion Books, 2007.

MacInnis, Bo and Jon A. Krosnick. *Climate Insights 2020: Partisan Divide, A Breakdown of Survey Results by Party Shows That Although the Views of Democrats, Republicans, and Independents Differ, They Also Converge in Ways That May Be Unexpected.* Resources for the Future. October 13,2020. *https://www.rff.org/publications/reports/climateinsights2020-partisan-divide.*

Wohlleben, Peter, and Jane Billinghurst. *The Heartbeat of Trees: Embracing Our Ancient Bond With Forests and Nature* Vancouver: Greystone Books, 2021.

CHAPTER FOUR: JUST SAY NO TO JARGON

Alda, Alan. *If I Understood You, Would I Have This Look on My Face? My Adventures in the Art and Science of Relating and Communicating.* New York: Random House, 2017.

Alan Alda Center for Communicating Science. "Home Page." Accessed October 1, 2021. *https://www.aldacenter.org.*

Bullock, Olivia M., Daniel Colón Amill, Hillary C. Shulman, and Graham N. Dixon. "Jargon as a Barrier to Effective Science Communication: Evidence from Metacognition." *Public Understanding of Science* 28, no. 7 (October, 2019): 845-853. doi:10.1177/0963662519865687.

Helfand, David J. *A Survival Guide to the Misinformation Age: Scientific Habits of Mind.* New York, NY: Columbia University Press, 2016.

Kornei, Katherine. Are You Confused by Scientific Jargon? So Are Scientists. *New York Times,* April 9, 2021. *https://www.nytimes.com/2021/04/09/science/science-jargon-caves.html.*

Markowitz, David M. "What Words Are Worth: National Science Foundation Grant Abstracts Indicate Award Funding." *Journal of Language and Social Psychology* 38, no. 3 (June 2019): 264–82. *https://doi.org/10.1177/0261927X18824859.*

Martinez, Alejandro and Stefano Mammola. "Specialized Terminology Reduces the Number of Citations of Scientific Papers." *Proceedings of the Royal Society B* 1948, no. 288 (April 7, 2021). *https://royalsocietypublishing.org/doi/full/10.1098/rspb.2020.2581.*

Merriam-Webster. s.v. "Circumlocution (n.)." Accessed September, 25 2021. *https://www.merriam-webster.com/dictionary/circumlocution.*

Merriam-Webster. s.v. "Jargon (n.)." Accessed September 25, 2021. *https://www.merriam-webster.com/dictionary/jargon.*

National Science Foundation. "Plain Language." Accessed October 1, 2021. *https://www.nsf.gov/policies/nsf_plain_language.jsp.*

Shulman, Hillary C., Graham N. Dixon, Olivia M. Bullock, and Daniel Colón Amill. "The Effects of Jargon on Processing Fluency, Self-Perceptions, and Scientific Engagement." *Journal of Language and Social Psychology* 39, no. 5-6 (January, 2020): 579-597. DOI: 10.1177/0261927X20902177.

CHAPTER FIVE: THE SCIENCE OF STORY AND THE STORY OF SCIENCE

Croston, Glenn. "The Thing We Fear More Than Death: Why Predators Are Responsible for Our Fear of Public Speaking." *Psychology Today*, November 29, 2012. *https://www.psychologytoday.com/us/blog/the-real-story-risk/201211/the-thing-we-fear-more-death.*

Duarte, Nancy. *Data Story: Explain Data and Inspire Action Through Story.* Oakton, VA: IdeaPress Publishing, 2019.

Hans Rosling. "The Best Hans Rosling Talks You've Ever Seen." February, 2016. Video, 19:36. *https://www.ted.com/playlists/474/the_best_hans_rosling_talks_yo.*

Helfand, D. J. *A Survival Guide to the Misinformation Age: Scientific Habits of Mind.* [United States]: Columbia University Press, 2016.

Renken, Elena. "How Stories Connect and Persuade Us: Unleashing The Brain Power Of Narrative." National Public Radio (NPR), April 11, 2020. *https://www.npr.org/sections/health-shots/2020/04/11/815573198/how-stories-connect-and-persuade-us-unleashing-the-brain-power-of-narrative.*

Sinek, Simon. *Start with Why: How Great Leaders Inspire Everyone to Take Action.* New York: Portfolio, 2009.

Thunberg, Greta. "The Disarming Case to Act Right Now on Climate Change", 2019. Video 11:12. *https://www.ted.com/talks/greta_thunberg_the_disarming_case_to_act_right_now_on_climate_change.*

United States Geological Survey (USGS). "How Much Carbon Dioxide Does the United States and the World Emit Each Year from Energy Sources?" 2019. Accessed August 5, 2021. *https://www.usgs.gov/faqs/how-much-carbon-dioxide-does-united-states-and-world-emit-each-year-energy-sources?qt-news_science_products=0#qt-news_science_products.*

CHAPTER SIX: VISUALIZATION

Duarte, Nancy. *Resonate: Present Visual Stories That Transform Audiences.* Hoboken, N.J.: John Wiley & Sons, 2010.

Jasinski, David, Paula Jasinski, and Robert Wood. *Chesapeake Bay Ecosystem Atlas: An Interactive Guide to Chesapeake Bay.* Richmond, Virginia: Chesapeake Environmental Communications, 2017. *http://books.apple.com/us/book/id1020777102.*

Kouyoumdjian, Haig. "Learning Through Visuals: Visual Imagery in the Classroom." *Psychology Today,* July 20, 2012. *https://www.psychologytoday.com/us/blog/get-psyched/201207/learning-through-visuals.*

Tufte, Edward. *The Visual Display of Quantitative Information.* Cheshire, Connecticut: Graphics Press, 1983.